Mastering Intervals

Edition 3

- ✦ Recognize any interval by site & sound
- ✦ Intermediate to advanced levels
- ✦ Answer Manual included

Barry Michael Wehrli

Mastering Intervals

Edition 3

 The letter C with a circle around it stands for the word **copyright**.

Copyright is made up of two words:
Copy: To make a picture of or create another of something.
Right: Permission to own, create or use something.

The copyright on this book protects the rights of its publisher to copy, sell, give away, make changes in, or publicly show the book to others. To do so without the publisher's written permission violates the publisher's rights.

The **copyright notice** is the copyright symbol, the date of publication, and the name of the publisher, as shown at the top of this page.

Cutting-Edge Books and Products
for the Music Teacher and Retailer

12830 Burbank Boulevard, Box 204, Valley Village, CA 91607-1402 www.wehrlipubs.com

Cover designed by Sandy Fox, eMedia Solutions, Inc.

Foreword

Traditional music theory teaches us that music has three elements: melody, harmony and rhythm. Upon closer inspection, however, it can be seen that melody (notes played in succession) and harmony (notes played simultaneously) both share a more fundamental element called the "interval". Therefore, music can be reduced to only two elements: intervals and rhythm. These two elements, blending together, produce music and are essentially what evoke thought, feeling and interpretation in the listener.

Traditional music theory also teaches us the intervals of the *scale*, in which the distance from the scale *tonic* to each successive scale *degree* is given a name. In addition to learning the relationship between a scale and its relative intervals, musicians should also have an independent knowledge of intervals, as real-world situations will require them to see, hear or think of intervals outside of a scale context. Three examples illustrate this point:

1. A fellow musician may ask you to play or sing "a major 3rd above". The fastest way to comply is to simply know the interval, without stepping-your-way up to the pitch through scale tones.
2. Chords are built using intervals that relate to the *root* of the chord, not to the tonic of a scale (unless the chord root and scale tonic happen to be the same pitch).
3. Musical ideas are not necessarily thought of in relation to any scale, particularly when those ideas extend beyond the confined pitch "palette" of any one scale. The ultimate means of determining the correct pitches in a melody or harmony is pure, interval perception.

Although there is not a great deal of theory to the subject of intervals, successful understanding and use of intervals comes only with sufficient drilling and practical exercises. Numerous activities in all facets of this subject are provided, including activities that develop instant recognition of intervals, both on the keyboard and by ear. Musical excerpts in various styles are analyzed for their interval content, providing insight on melodic and harmonic tendencies in music. In these excerpts, additional music theory elements are presented to further enhance one's musical intellect. The Answer Manual confirms accuracy and understanding.

Knowing intervals "cold" increases skill in music theory, sight-reading, composition and improvisation. **Mastering Intervals** is a unique and thorough study of the subject, providing the benefits and abilities described above.

About the Author

Barry Michael Wehrli began piano and keyboard studies at the age of eight. His formal training includes instruction from Dolores Rhoads, Terry Trotter and John Novello and music studies at California State University, Northridge. He composes, arranges and records at his home studio, is a freelance performer, heads Wehrli Publications and teaches piano and electronic music. His clients include Warner Brothers, Yamaha, and local professional musicians and teachers.

Many Thanks

To my parents and teachers for nurturing and cultivating my love of music.

To my wonderful wife for her valuable assistance in creating this book.

Prerequisites

- A piano or keyboard for daily study.

- Familiarity with the following musical terms:

Notehead	*Pitch*	*Melody*
Stem	*Sharp*	*Rhythm*
Treble clef	*Flat*	*Time signature*
Bass clef	*Double sharp*	*Key signature*
Half step/semitone	*Double flat*	*Scale*
Whole step/whole tone	*Natural*	*Scale degrees*
Middle C	*Accidental*	*Major scale*

Some of these terms are defined in the glossary. Others can be found in music dictionaries or notation manuals, of which any serious musician should own at least one.

How to use this Book

- Set up a workable, consistent study schedule and stick to it. Steady progress improves understanding and the ability to apply what you learn.

- A Workshop Checksheet begins each workshop, introducing its topics and project list. Read the topics and project list before starting the workshop. The checkbox next to each project is checked off by the teacher or self-study student, when completed. To achieve the goals of each workshop, complete the projects in the order presented.

- Make sure all words, symbols and concepts are fully understood. Use a dictionary to clear up words as you read.

- Additional terms not defined within the text are in the glossary on pages 146 - 147.

- If a confusion occurs or a particular mistake recurs in the answers, return to the appropriate section of the book and look for a misunderstood word or symbol in that area. If it cannot be found there, search earlier or later until you find the misunderstood word or symbol. Use a dictionary to clear up all of its definitions, using each in sentences. Then restudy from that point forward in the text. Repeat as needed, until the problem is resolved.

- Answers for each written activity are to be checked and corrected before continuing on to the next activity.

- Answers to all written work are provided in the **Answer Manual** on pages 107 - 144.

Answer Manual

- The corresponding page number is given below each activity name.

- Answers should be identical to those given in this book, unless stated otherwise. Check answers for the following, as applicable:
    - notehead position on the staff,
    - accidental placement,
    - stem direction,
    - stem length,
    - capitalized "P", "M" and "A" for perfect, major or augmented interval names,
    - lower-case "m" and "d" for minor or diminished interval names.

- The order of the answers may vary for some activities.

- Accidentals in parentheses are optional. They are given here to clarify that a repeated note remains sharped, flatted, etc., because it is in the same measure. Such answers, even without the accidental are still correct, per standard music notation rules.

Mastering Intervals
Edition 3

Table of Contents

Workshop 1 Checksheet 1

    Melodic & Harmonic Intervals 3

    Interval Numbers 8

    Interval Qualities 14

    Perfect Intervals 16

    Major Intervals 24

    Minor Intervals 32

    Augmented Intervals 44

    Diminished Intervals 52

    Interval Review 62

Workshop 2 Checksheet 67

    Consonant & Dissonant Intervals 69

    Enharmonics 70

    Mixed Interval Final Exam 72

    Harmonic Inversion 76

    Mirror Inversion 80

    Simple & Compound Intervals 82

    Compound Interval Inversion 86

Workshop 3 Checksheet 89

    Music Analyses 91

Answer Manual 107

Interval Ear Training Resources 145

Glossary 146

Bibliography 148

Mastering Intervals
Edition 3

Workshop 1 Checksheet

- *Melodic & Harmonic Intervals*
- *Interval Numbers*
- *Interval Qualities*
- *Perfect Intervals*
- *Major Intervals*
- *Minor Intervals*
- *Augmented Intervals*
- *Diminished Intervals*

✓	**PROJECTS**
☐	1. Melodic & Harmonic Intervals and Activity #1
☐	2. Stemming Intervals and Activities #1 - 2
☐	3. Interval Numbers and Activities #1 - 6
☐	4. Interval Qualities
☐	5. Writing Intervals on the Staff
☐	6. Perfect Intervals and Activities #1 - 4
☐	7. Keyboard Activities #1 - 2 and Perfect Interval Activity #5
☐	8. Ear Training Activities #1A - 1D
☐	9. Major Intervals and Activities #1 - 3
☐	10. Keyboard Activities #3 - 6 and Major Interval Activity #4
☐	11. Ear Training Activities #2A - 2D
☐	12. Minor Intervals and Activities #1 - 3
☐	13. Keyboard Activities #7 - 9 and Minor Interval Activity #4
☐	14. Ear Training Activities #3A - 3D
☐	15. Mixed Interval Activities #1 - 5
☐	16. Augmented Intervals and Activities #1 - 3
☐	17. Keyboard Activity #10 and Augmented Interval Activity #4

(over)

✓ **PROJECTS**

- [ ] 18. Ear Training Activities #4A - 4B
- [ ] 19. Diminished Intervals and Activities #1 - 4
- [ ] 20. Mixed Interval Activities #6 - 9
- [ ] 21. Ear Training Activities #5A - 5D
- [ ] 22. Interval Review
- [ ] 23. Mixed Interval Activities #10 - 12

Melodic & Harmonic Intervals

Interval: The distance from one note (or key) to another.

An interval can be played in two different ways.
1. **Melodic interval:** Two notes played one after the other, or separately.
2. **Harmonic interval:** Two notes played at the same time, or together.

Examples of harmonic and melodic intervals.

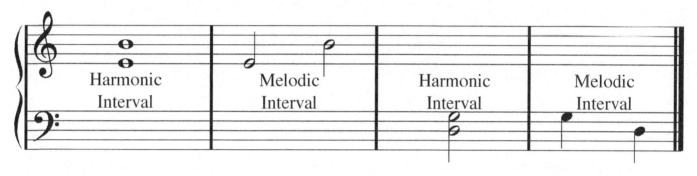

MELODIC & HARMONIC INTERVAL ACTIVITY #1

In each box below, write **M** if the interval is melodic or **H** if the interval is harmonic.

Stemming Melodic Intervals

Stems follow the rules of **direction, length** and **note placement** to ensure that notes and intervals are easy to read.

- Stems are **up** on the **right** side of the notehead.
- Stems are **down** on the **left** side of the notehead.

Dots are placed on the **right** side of the notehead.

STEM DIRECTION

1. The stem can point in **either direction** when the notehead is **on** the center line of the staff (line 3), but is commonly drawn downward.

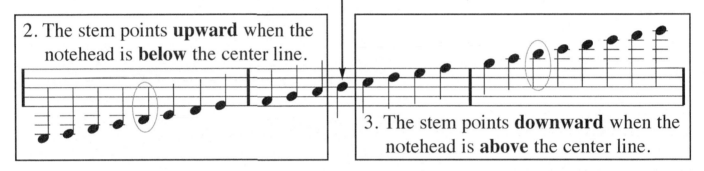

2. The stem points **upward** when the notehead is **below** the center line.

3. The stem points **downward** when the notehead is **above** the center line.

STEM LENGTH

1. Notes from the second space below the staff to the second space above the staff have a stem length of **3 staff spaces**. The circled notes above mark this range.

2. Notes above or below this range have stems that extend at least to the **center line**.

Stemming Harmonic Intervals

A single stem joins the two noteheads of a harmonic interval.

STEM DIRECTION

1. For harmonic intervals with noteheads the **same distance** from the center line of the staff (line 3), the stem can point **either up or down**.

2. For harmonic intervals with noteheads **not** the same distance from the center line of the staff, the note farthest from line 3 determines the stem direction.

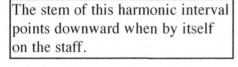

This note is farthest from line 3. Stem the interval upward.

This note is farthest from line 3. Stem the interval downward.

3. Musical context can also determine stem direction.

The stem of this harmonic interval points downward when by itself on the staff.

However, its stem direction can be changed to match the direction of surrounding intervals. This makes the interval easier to read.

STEM LENGTH

1. Harmonic intervals inside the staff have a stem length of 3 staff spaces beyond the note nearest the stem ending.

2. Harmonic intervals outside the staff have stems that extend at least to the center line of the staff.

3. Harmonic intervals with noteheads both inside and outside the staff have stem lengths that go beyond the center line and are 3 staff spaces from the note nearest the stem ending.

NOTE PLACEMENT ON THE STEM

Harmonic intervals with a line note placed next to a space note have the **higher pitch note** placed on the **right** and the **lower pitch note** on the **left**, regardless of stem direction. The note farthest from line 3 determines the stem direction.

Stemming Intervals Activity #1

1. Stem the melodic intervals below.

2. Stem the harmonic intervals below.

Stemming Intervals Activity #2

Circle the harmonic intervals that are stemmed incorrectly.

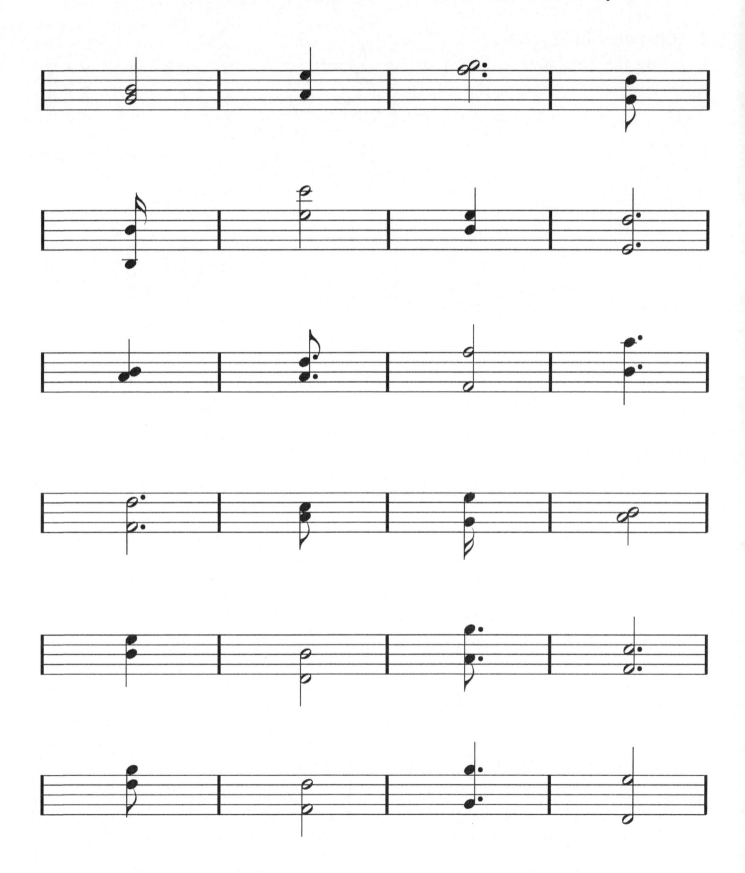

Interval Numbers

A number is used to name the distance between two notes or two keys.
Both notes or keys of the interval are included in measuring this distance.

1. **Harmonic intervals:**
   Count the lines and spaces up or down from one note to the other. The two notes of the interval are included.

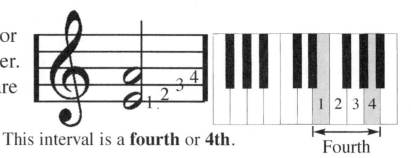

This interval is a **fourth** or **4th**.

2. **Melodic intervals:**
   Count the lines and spaces up or down from the first note to the second. The two notes of the interval are included.

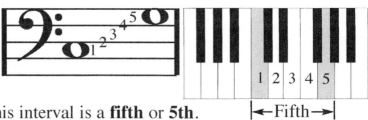

This interval is a **fifth** or **5th**.

Unison: This word comes from the Latin words *uni* meaning "one" and *sonus* meaning "sound". Unison means the two notes "are one". Their pitch is the same and their noteheads are in the same position on the staff. "Unison" is used instead of "first".

Octave: This word comes from the Latin word *octo* meaning "eight". It is the distance from one note to the next note of the **same name**. "Octave" is used instead of "eighth".

INTERVAL NUMBER ACTIVITY #1

Count the lines and spaces of each interval below to arrive at the given number. Then play and count the distance of each interval on the keyboard.

1st	2nd	3rd	4th	5th	6th	7th	8th
Unison	Second	Third	Fourth	Fifth	Sixth	Seventh	Octave

Interval Number Activity #2

1. Circle the unisons in red.
2. Circle the 2nds in blue.
3. Circle the 3rds in green.
4. Circle the 4ths in black.

5. Circle the 5ths in purple.
6. Circle the 6ths in orange.
7. Circle the 7ths in brown.
8. Circle the octaves in yellow.

Interval Number Activity #3

Write the interval numbers in the boxes below.

Interval Number Activity #4

1. Draw the **melodic** intervals shown below, starting on various natural notes. Use different note values (o ♩ ♪ ♩· ♪ etc.).

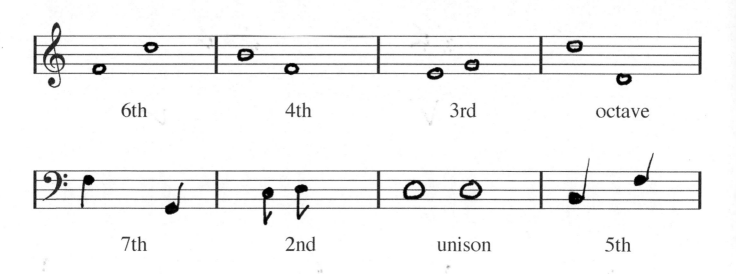

| 6th | 4th | 3rd | octave |

| 7th | 2nd | unison | 5th |

2. Draw the **harmonic** intervals shown below, starting on various natural notes. Use different note values (o ♩ ♪ ♩· ♪ etc.).

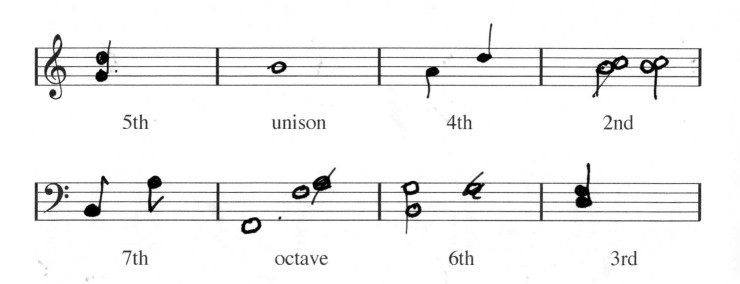

| 5th | unison | 4th | 2nd |

| 7th | octave | 6th | 3rd |

Interval Number Activity #5

Shade in the correct key **above and below** the keys with dots.

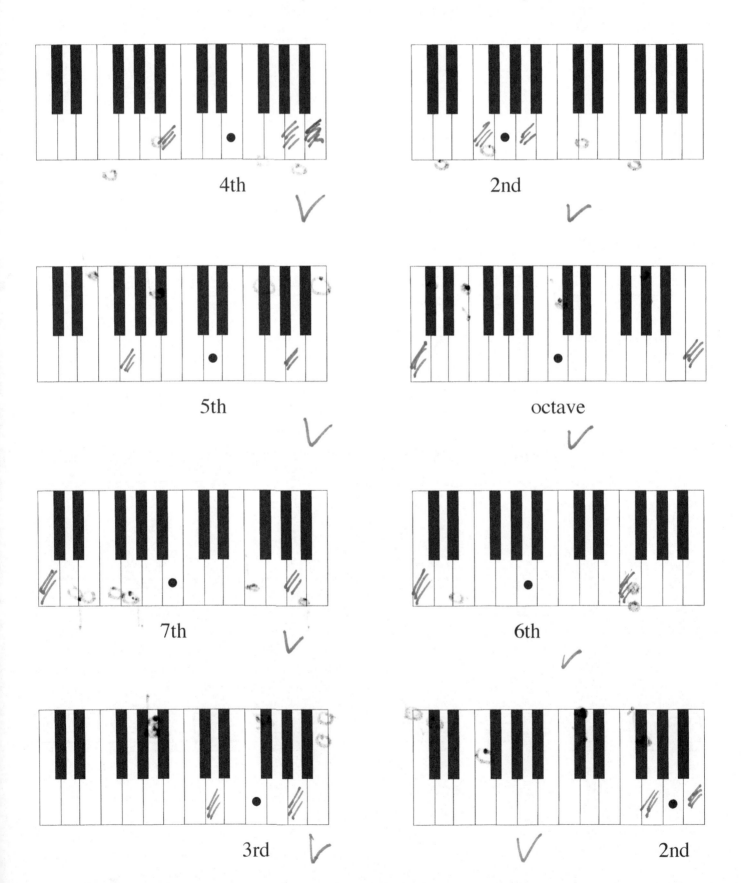

4th

2nd

5th

octave

7th

6th

3rd

2nd

Interval Number Activity #6

Complete the following statements from memory, without looking at the keyboard.

1. A 6th above a C is ___A___ ✓.

2. A 2nd below an F is ___E___ ✓.

3. A 4th above a D is ___G___ ✓.

4. An octave below a B is ___B___ ✓.

5. A 3rd above an A is ___C___ ✓.

6. A 7th below a G is ___A___ ✓.

7. The unison of D is ___D___ ✓.

8. A 5th below a C is ___F___ ✓.

9. A 4th below an E is ___B___ ✓.

10. A 3rd below an A is ___F___ ✓.

11. A 7th above an F is ___E___ ✓.

12. A 2nd above a B is ___C___ ✓.

13. An octave below a G is ___G___ ✓.

14. A 6th below a B is ___D___ ✓.

15. A 5th above an E is ___B___ ✓.

16. The unison of C is ___C___ ✓.

17. A 2nd below a C is ___B___ ✓.

18. A 7th above an A is ___G___ ✓.

19. A 4th below an F is ___C___ ✓.

20. A 3rd above a D is ___F___ ✓.

21. A 5th above a B is ___F___ ✓.

22. An octave above an E is ___E___ ✓.

23. A 6th below an F is ___A___ ✓.

24. The unison of G is ___G___ ✓.

25. A 7th below a D is ___E___ ✓.

26. A 5th below an A is ___D___ ✓.

27. A 3rd above a B is ___D___ ✓.

28. A 2nd above a G is ___A___ ✓.

29. A 6th above an E is ___C___ ✓.

30. An octave below a D is ___D___ ✓.

Interval Qualities

Compare the interval in each measure below.

Counting the lines and spaces of these notes, we find that both intervals are 7ths, but one has B♮ and the other has B♭. The difference is the **number of half steps**; middle C to B♮ is 11 half steps, but middle C to B♭ is 10 half steps. Count the half steps on the keyboard to see this. (Keep in mind that the term "half step" implies movement; one must move away from the starting key or note before the first half step can be counted.)

Examine the two intervals below.

These intervals are also 7ths, even though the B is sharped in the first measure (producing 12 half steps) and double flatted in the second (producing 9 half steps).

Accidentals do not change the interval number. Remember this!
The interval number is determined only by the inclusive distance from one (natural) notehead to the other, or from one (natural) key to the other.

Each 7th interval above differs in the number of half steps. So how are these different 7th intervals distinguished? To precisely name these or any interval, the correct half step amount must be considered along with the interval number. This introduces the term "quality".

Quality: A word or letter showing the exact type of unison, 2nd, 3rd, 4th, 5th, 6th, 7th or octave. These are the five qualities and their letter representations:

1. perfect (P)
2. major (M)
3. minor (m)
4. augmented (A)
5. diminished (d)

These qualities and their companion interval numbers are explained in Workshop 1.

Writing Intervals on the Staff

For activities requiring notation on the staff, remember the following three steps:

1. Use the interval number to determine the note's position on the staff (as done in the preceding activities).
2. Use the interval quality to determine the number of half steps from one note to the other.
3. Add an accidental to the note drawn, if needed.

Example: Draw the melodic interval a perfect 4th above this note.

(Perfect 4th intervals have 5 half steps, as you will learn on the next page.)

Step 1:
Since the interval is a **4th above** the given note, the notehead must be drawn in the third staff space.

Step 2:
Since the interval is a **perfect** 4th, count 5 half steps up from the E♭. This will be the black key just below the A. The correct name of that key is A♭. (It is not G♯ because the interval of E♭ to G♯ is some type of 3rd and the notehead would be drawn on the second staff line.)

Step 3:
Since the answer is A♭, draw a flat next to the A.

NOTE:

The above answer could also be derived by correlation to a known *scale*.
A perfect 4th above E♭ must be A♭ since A♭ is the fourth *scale degree* of the E♭ *Major scale* (see italicized terms in the glossary on pages 146 - 147).

Perfect Intervals

- Perfect intervals are unisons, 4ths, 5ths, and octaves.
- A capital "P" and the numbers 1, 4, 5, and 8 will represent this interval.
- The 1st, 4th, and 5th major scale degrees form perfect intervals.

How it is said:	Perfect Unison	Perfect Fourth	Perfect Fifth	Perfect Octave
How it is written:	P1	P4	P5	P8
Major scale degree:	1	4	5	(1)

Number of half steps:	0	5	7	12

PERFECT INTERVAL ACTIVITY #1

Memorize the number of half steps for each of the four perfect intervals above.
When you can recite these without hesitation, go on to Activity #2 below.

PERFECT INTERVAL ACTIVITY #2

Write the correct interval name in each box below. Then play these intervals.

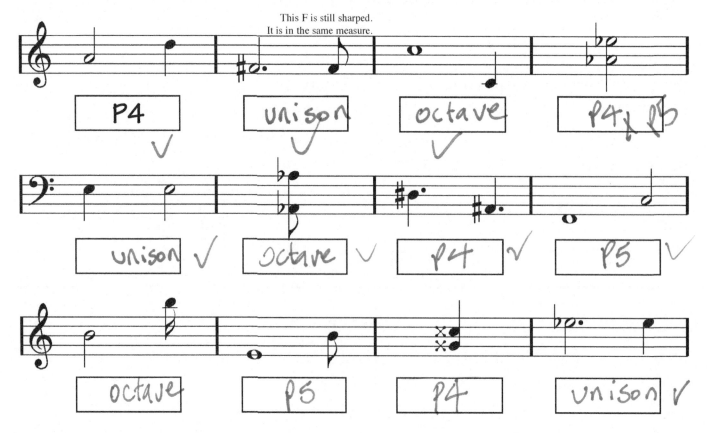

This F is still sharped.
It is in the same measure.

P4 ✓	unison ✓	octave ✓	P4 + P5

unison ✓	octave ✓	P4 ✓	P5 ✓

octave	P5	P4	unison ✓

Perfect Interval Activity #3

1. Draw the melodic interval a **perfect 4th (P4) above** each note. Then play these.

2. Draw the melodic interval a **perfect 4th (P4) below** each note. Then play these.

3. Draw the melodic interval a **perfect 5th (P5) above** each note. Then play these.

4. Draw the melodic interval a **perfect 5th (P5) below** each note. Then play these.

5. Draw the melodic interval a **perfect octave (P8) above** each note. Then play these.

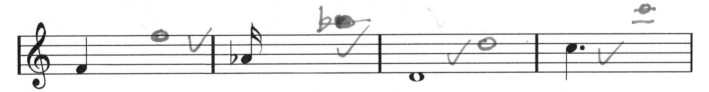

6. Draw the melodic interval a **perfect octave (P8) below** each note. Then play these.

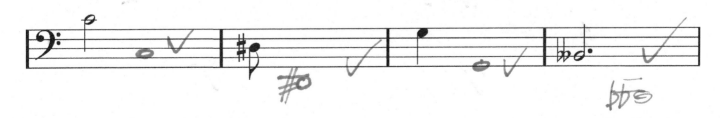

Perfect Interval Activity #4

Shade in the correct key **above and below** the keys with dots. For the unison, just shade in the correct key.

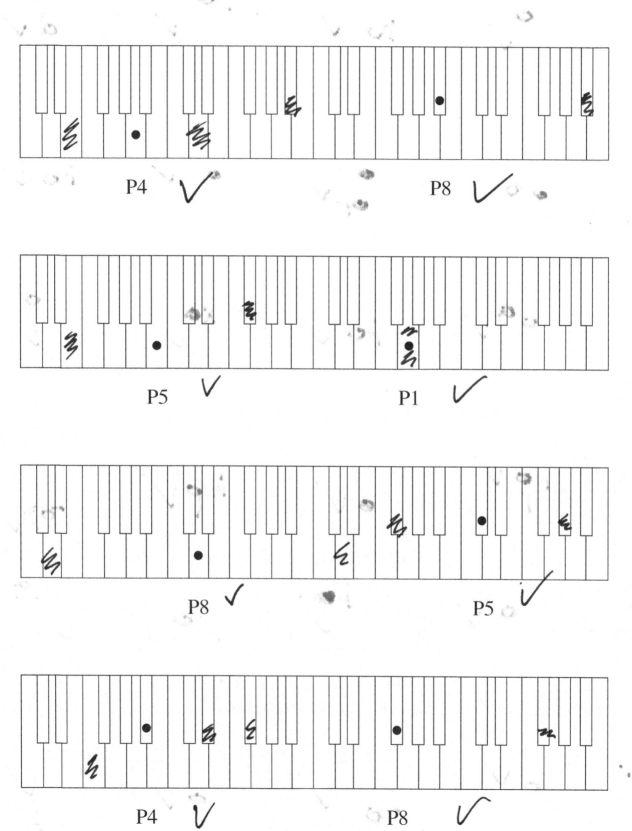

Keyboard Activity Guide

The keyboard activities develop instant recognition of intervals on the keyboard.
Remember the following rules for all keyboard activities in this book.

- For each Part (A, B, C, etc.), start with the left hand at the bottom of the keyboard, then switch to the right hand near middle C and continue on to the highest key. Going back down, switch to the left hand near middle C and continue on to the starting key. Use finger 2 in each hand.
- Practice each Part until it can be played quickly and accurately without any need to count the distance between keys. Then continue on.
- Practice the Random step until there is no hesitation in playing or naming the correct keys, both above and below every chosen key.
- Complete all keyboard activities for each interval quality before continuing on to the next.

KEYBOARD ACTIVITY #1

Part A

1. Find the lowest C key on the keyboard.
2. From that key, play consecutive **perfect 4ths** all the way across the keyboard.
3. Begin back down the same way, to the lowest C.

Random

1. Randomly pick a key on the keyboard and name it.
2. Play a perfect 4th above and below the chosen key, naming each correctly.
3. Repeat steps 1 and 2 using many different keys.

KEYBOARD ACTIVITY #2

Part A

1. Find the lowest C key on the keyboard.
2. From that key, play consecutive **perfect 5ths** all the way across the keyboard.
3. Begin back down the same way, to the lowest C.

Random

1. Randomly pick a key on the keyboard and name it.
2. Play a perfect 5th above and below the chosen key, naming each correctly.
3. Repeat steps 1 and 2 using many different keys.

Perfect Interval Activity #5

Complete the following statements from memory, without looking at the keyboard. The first two are done as examples.

1. A P5 above a B♯ is ___F×___.

2. A P8 below an F is ___F___.

3. A P4 above an A is ___D___ ✓.

4. The P1 of a B is ___B___ ✓.

5. A P5 below an E♭ is ___A♭___ ✓.

6. A P8 above a G is ___G___ ✓.

7. A P4 below a D♯ is ___A♯___ ✓.

8. The P1 of a C is ___C___ ✓.

9. A P4 above an F is ___B (B♭)___ ✗.

10. A P4 below an A♭ is ___E♭___ ✓.

11. The P1 of an A♯ is ___A♯___ ✓.

12. A P8 above a C♯ is ___G♯___ ✓.

13. A P4 above a G♭♭ is ___C♭♭___ ✓.

14. The P1 of a D♭ is ___D♭___ ✓.

15. A P5 below an A is ___D___ ✓.

16. A P8 above a G♯ is ___G♯___ ✓.

17. The P1 of an E is ___E___ ✓.

18. A P4 below a C is ___G___ ✓.

19. A P5 above an F♯ is ___C♯___ ✓.

20. A P8 below a C× is ___C×___ ✓.

Ear Training Activity Guide

The ear training activities develop instant recognition of intervals by sound. Most ear training activities are presented in groups of four, labeled A through D, such as 1A, 1B, 1C, 1D or 2A, 2B, 2C, 2D, etc.

Apply the following points to all ear training activities in this book.

• The A and C activities require a partner who is familiar with interval theory. A partner working through his/her own **Mastering Intervals** book at the same time can accelerate ear training for both of you. (If no partner is available, choose one of the many ear training products listed in the Interval Ear Training Resources on page 145 to achieve the purposes of the A and C activities.)

• Do each step in the exact order given. Do not skip steps.

• Be sure your partner plays in the middle area of the keyboard, only.

• "Name each interval" means to call out the **quality and number**. Examples: "Perfect Octave" or "Perfect 5th".

• If your answer is wrong, your partner plays the interval repeatedly until you guess the correct interval name.

• To aid concentration and prevent visual distractions, you may close your eyes when listening to the intervals played by your partner.

• The B and D activities are vocal activities which do not require a partner. Mark the highest and lowest white keys you can comfortably sing on the keyboard below for reference when doing any B or D activity.

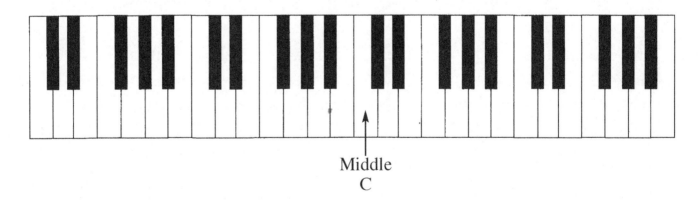

Middle
C

• When singing pitches, keep your mouth open and use either "ah" or "oh" as your singing vowel. Another option is to sing the name of each pitch, which further improves pitch recognition.

• Complete each group of ear training activities before starting the next. Finish #1A - #1D before starting #2A - #2D, etc.

EAR TRAINING ACTIVITY #1A

1. Listen to your partner play perfect intervals melodically **up** from middle C in ascending order: P1, P4, P5, P8. Repeat this until each interval is familiar.

2. Have your partner play perfect intervals in random order while you name each aloud. Continue until you have correctly named at least 10 perfect intervals in a row up from middle C.

3. Listen to perfect intervals played melodically up from another key in ascending order: P1, P4, P5, P8. Repeat this until each interval is familiar.

4. Have your partner play perfect intervals in random order while you name each aloud. Continue until you have correctly named at least 10 perfect intervals in a row up from the chosen key.

5. Repeat steps 3 and 4 on other keys, chosen by your partner, until you can correctly name every perfect interval up from three different starting keys.

EAR TRAINING ACTIVITY #1B

1. Play a key near the bottom of your singing range. (This chosen key is played repeatedly throughout steps 2 and 3 to maintain pitch reference.)

2. Sing each of the four perfect intervals **up** from the chosen pitch, in order: P1, P4, P5, P8. Sing both notes of each interval (the bottom pitch and the answer above). If you have trouble, play the upper key very briefly as a hint. Repeat this until you can correctly sing all four intervals at least twice through without reference to the keyboard.

3. Call out various perfect intervals in random order, singing the notes of each interval aloud. Continue this until you can correctly sing 10 intervals in a row up from the same chosen pitch.

4. Repeat steps 1 - 3 using different lower-range keys until you can easily sing every perfect interval up from three different starting keys.

EAR TRAINING ACTIVITY #1C

1. Listen to your partner play perfect intervals melodically **down** from middle C in descending order: P1, P4, P5, P8. Repeat this until each interval is familiar.

2. Have your partner play perfect intervals in random order while you name each aloud. Continue until you have correctly named at least 10 perfect intervals in a row down from middle C.

3. Listen to perfect intervals played melodically down from another key in descending order: P1, P4, P5, P8. Repeat this until each interval is familiar.

4. Have your partner play perfect intervals in random order while you name each aloud. Continue until you have correctly named at least 10 perfect intervals in a row down from the chosen key.

5. Repeat steps 3 and 4 on other keys, chosen by your partner, until you can correctly name every perfect interval down from three different starting keys.

EAR TRAINING ACTIVITY #1D

1. Play a key near the top of your singing range. (This chosen key is played repeatedly throughout steps 2 and 3 to maintain pitch reference.)

2. Sing each of the four perfect intervals **down** from the chosen pitch, in order: P1, P4, P5, P8. Sing both notes of each interval (the top pitch and the answer below). If you have trouble, play the lower key very briefly as a hint. Repeat this until you can correctly sing all four intervals at least twice through without reference to the keyboard.

3. Call out various perfect intervals in random order, singing the notes of each interval aloud. Continue this until you can correctly sing 10 intervals in a row down from the same chosen pitch.

4. Repeat steps 1 - 3 using different upper-range keys until you can easily sing every perfect interval down from three different starting keys.

Major Intervals

- Major intervals are 2nds, 3rds, 6ths, and 7ths.
- A capital "M" and the numbers 2, 3, 6, and 7 will represent this interval.
- The 2nd, 3rd, 6th, and 7th major scale degrees form major intervals.

How it is said:	Major Second	Major Third	Major Sixth	Major Seventh
How it is written:	M2	M3	M6	M7
Major scale degree:	2	3	6	7

| Number of half steps: | 2 | 4 | 9 | 11 |

MAJOR INTERVAL ACTIVITY #1

Memorize the number of half steps for each of the four major intervals above. When you can recite these without hesitation, go on to Activity #2 below.

MAJOR INTERVAL ACTIVITY #2

1. Draw the melodic interval a **major 2nd (M2) above** each note. Then play these.

2. Draw the melodic interval a **major 2nd (M2) below** each note. Then play these.

3. Draw the melodic interval a **major 3rd (M3) above** each note. Then play these.

4. Draw the melodic interval a **major 3rd (M3) below** each note. Then play these.

5. Draw the melodic interval a **major 6th (M6) above** each note. Then play these.

6. Draw the melodic interval a **major 6th (M6) below** each note. Then play these.

7. Draw the melodic interval a **major 7th (M7) above** each note. Then play these.

8. Draw the melodic interval a **major 7th (M7) below** each note. Then play these.

Major Interval Activity #3

Shade in the correct key **above and below** the keys with dots.

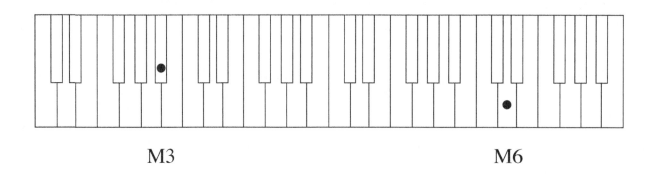

M3   M6

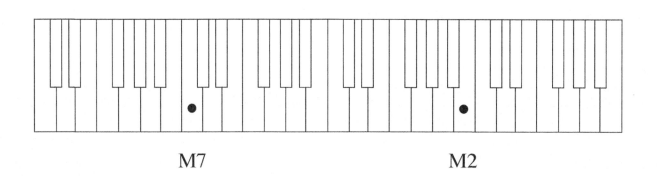

M7   M2

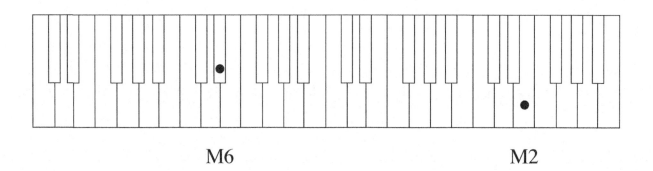

M6   M2

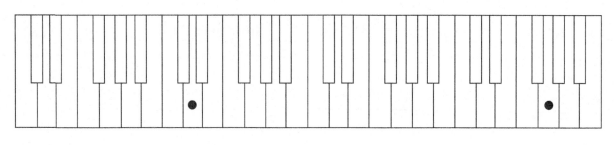

M7   M3

KEYBOARD ACTIVITY #3
Part A
1. Find the lowest C key on the keyboard.
2. From that key, play consecutive **major 2nds** all the way across the keyboard.
3. Begin back down the same way, to the lowest C.

Part B
1. Find the lowest D♭ key on the keyboard.
2. From that key, play consecutive **major 2nds** all the way across the keyboard.
3. Begin back down the same way, to the lowest D♭.

Random
1. Randomly pick a key on the keyboard and name it.
2. Play a major 2nd above and below the chosen key, naming each correctly.
3. Repeat steps 1 and 2 using many different keys.

KEYBOARD ACTIVITY #4
Part A
1. Find the lowest C key on the keyboard.
2. From that key, play consecutive **major 3rds** all the way across the keyboard.
3. Begin back down the same way, to the lowest C.

Part B
1. Find the lowest D♭ key on the keyboard.
2. From that key, play consecutive **major 3rds** all the way across the keyboard.
3. Begin back down the same way, to the lowest D♭.

Part C
1. Find the lowest D key on the keyboard.
2. From that key, play consecutive **major 3rds** all the way across the keyboard.
3. Begin back down the same way, to the lowest D.

Part D
1. Find the lowest E♭ key on the keyboard.
2. From that key, play consecutive **major 3rds** all the way across the keyboard.
3. Begin back down the same way, to the lowest E♭.

Random
1. Randomly pick a key on the keyboard and name it.
2. Play a major 3rd above and below the chosen key, naming each correctly.
3. Repeat steps 1 and 2 using many different keys.

KEYBOARD ACTIVITY #5

Part A

1. Find the lowest C key on the keyboard.
2. From that key, play consecutive **major 6ths** all the way across the keyboard.
3. Begin back down the same way, to the lowest C.

Part B

1. Find the lowest D♭ key on the keyboard.
2. From that key, play consecutive **major 6ths** all the way across the keyboard.
3. Begin back down the same way, to the lowest D♭.

Part C

1. Find the lowest D key on the keyboard.
2. From that key, play consecutive **major 6ths** all the way across the keyboard.
3. Begin back down the same way, to the lowest D.

Random

1. Randomly pick a key on the keyboard and name it.
2. Play a major 6th above and below the chosen key, naming each correctly.
3. Repeat steps 1 and 2 using many different keys.

KEYBOARD ACTIVITY #6

Part A

1. Find the lowest C key on the keyboard.
2. From that key, play consecutive **major 7ths** all the way across the keyboard.
3. Begin back down the same way, to the lowest C.

Part B

1. Find the lowest F key on the keyboard.
2. From that key, play consecutive **major 7ths** all the way across the keyboard.
3. Begin back down the same way, to the lowest F.

Random

1. Randomly pick a key on the keyboard and name it.
2. Play a major 7th above and below the chosen key, naming each correctly.
3. Repeat steps 1 and 2 using many different keys.

Major Interval Activity #4

Complete the following statements from memory, without looking at the keyboard.

1. A M3 above a B is _____.

2. A M7 below an F is _____.

3. A M2 above an A is _____.

4. A M6 below a B is _____.

5. A M3 below an E♭ is _____.

6. A M7 above a G is _____.

7. A M2 below a D♯ is _____.

8. A M6 above a C is _____.

9. A M3 above an A is _____.

10. A M7 below a D♭ is _____.

11. A M2 above an E is _____.

12. A M6 below a C♯ is _____.

13. A M3 below an F is _____.

14. A M7 above a D♭ is _____.

15. A M2 below an F✕ is _____.

16. A M6 above an A♭ is _____.

17. A M3 above an E is _____.

18. A M7 below a B♭♭ is _____.

19. A M2 above a G♯ is _____.

20. A M6 below an E♭ is _____.

EAR TRAINING ACTIVITY #2A

1. Listen to your partner play major intervals melodically **up** from middle C in ascending order: M2, M3, M6, M7. Repeat until each interval is familiar.

2. Have your partner play major intervals in random order while you name each aloud. Continue until you have correctly named at least 10 major intervals in a row up from middle C.

3. Listen to major intervals played melodically up from another key in ascending order: M2, M3, M6, M7. Repeat until each interval is familiar.

4. Have your partner play major intervals in random order while you name each aloud. Continue until you have correctly named at least 10 major intervals in a row up from the chosen key.

5. Repeat steps 3 and 4 on other keys, chosen by your partner, until you can correctly name every major interval up from three different starting keys.

EAR TRAINING ACTIVITY #2B

1. Play a key near the bottom of your singing range. (This chosen key is played repeatedly throughout steps 2 and 3 to maintain pitch reference.)

2. Sing each of the four major intervals **up** from the chosen pitch, in order: M2, M3, M6, M7. Sing both notes of each interval (the bottom pitch and the answer above). If you have trouble, play the upper key very briefly as a hint. Repeat this until you can correctly sing all four intervals at least twice through without reference to the keyboard.

3. Call out various major intervals in random order, singing the notes of each interval aloud. Continue this until you can correctly sing 10 intervals in a row up from the same chosen pitch.

4. Repeat steps 1 - 3 using different lower-range keys until you can easily sing every major interval up from three different starting keys.

EAR TRAINING ACTIVITY #2C

1. Listen to your partner play major intervals melodically **down** from middle C in descending order: M2, M3, M6, M7. Repeat until each interval is familiar.

2. Have your partner play major intervals in random order while you name each aloud. Continue until you have correctly named at least 10 major intervals in a row down from middle C.

3. Listen to major intervals played melodically down from another key in descending order: M2, M3, M6, M7. Repeat until each interval is familiar.

4. Have your partner play major intervals in random order while you name each aloud. Continue until you have correctly named at least 10 major intervals in a row down from the chosen key.

5. Repeat steps 3 and 4 on other keys, chosen by your partner, until you can correctly name every major interval down from three different starting keys.

EAR TRAINING ACTIVITY #2D

1. Play a key near the top of your singing range. (This chosen key is played repeatedly throughout steps 2 and 3 to maintain pitch reference.)

2. Sing each of the four major intervals **down** from the chosen pitch, in order: M2, M3, M6, M7. Sing both notes of each interval (the top pitch and the answer below). If you have trouble, play the lower key very briefly as a hint. Repeat this until you can correctly sing all four intervals at least twice through without reference to the keyboard.

3. Call out various major intervals in random order, singing the notes of each interval aloud. Continue this until you can correctly sing 10 intervals in a row down from the same chosen pitch.

4. Repeat steps 1 - 3 using different upper-range keys until you can easily sing every major interval down from three different starting keys.

Minor Intervals

- Minor intervals are 2nds, 3rds, 6ths, and 7ths, like the major intervals.
- Minor intervals are **one half step less** than major intervals.
- A lower-case "m" and the numbers 2, 3, 6, and 7 will represent this interval.

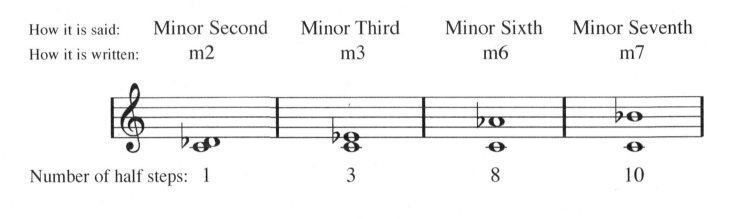

How it is said:	Minor Second	Minor Third	Minor Sixth	Minor Seventh
How it is written:	m2	m3	m6	m7
Number of half steps:	1	3	8	10

MINOR INTERVAL ACTIVITY #1

Memorize the number of half steps for each of the four minor intervals above. When you can recite these without hesitation, go on to Activity #2 below.

MINOR INTERVAL ACTIVITY #2

1. Draw the melodic interval a **minor 2nd (m2) above** each note. Then play these.

2. Draw the melodic interval a **minor 2nd (m2) below** each note. Then play these.

3. Draw the melodic interval a **minor 3rd (m3) above** each note. Then play these.

4. Draw the melodic interval a **minor 3rd (m3) below** each note. Then play these.

5. Draw the melodic interval a **minor 6th (m6) above** each note. Then play these.

6. Draw the melodic interval a **minor 6th (m6) below** each note. Then play these.

7. Draw the melodic interval a **minor 7th (m7) above** each note. Then play these.

8. Draw the melodic interval a **minor 7th (m7) below** each note. Then play these.

Minor Interval Activity #3

Shade in the correct key **above and below** the keys with dots.

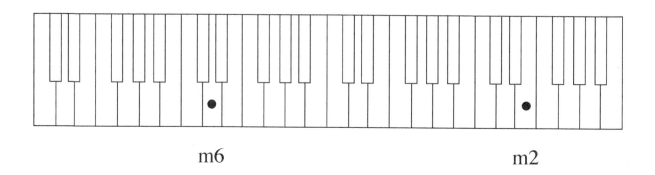

m6   m2

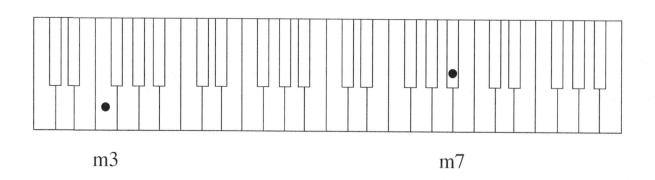

m3   m7

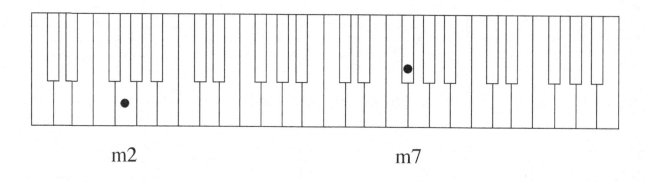

m2   m7

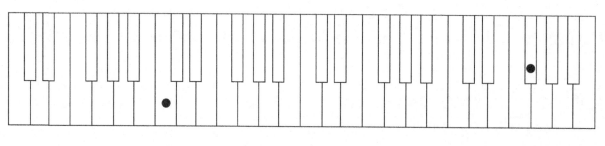

m6   m3

KEYBOARD ACTIVITY #7

Part A

1. Find the lowest C key on the keyboard.
2. From that key, play consecutive **minor 3rds** all the way across the keyboard.
3. Begin back down the same way, to the lowest C.

Part B

1. Find the lowest D♭ key on the keyboard.
2. From that key, play consecutive **minor 3rds** all the way across the keyboard.
3. Begin back down the same way, to the lowest D♭.

Part C

1. Find the lowest D key on the keyboard.
2. From that key, play consecutive **minor 3rds** all the way across the keyboard.
3. Begin back down the same way, to the lowest D.

Random

1. Randomly pick a key on the keyboard and name it.
2. Play a minor 3rd above and below the chosen key, naming each correctly.
3. Repeat steps 1 and 2 using many different keys.

KEYBOARD ACTIVITY #8

Part A

1. Find the lowest C key on the keyboard.
2. From that key, play consecutive **minor 6ths** all the way across the keyboard.
3. Begin back down the same way, to the lowest C.

Part B

1. Find the lowest D♭ key on the keyboard.
2. From that key, play consecutive **minor 6ths** all the way across the keyboard.
3. Begin back down the same way, to the lowest D♭.

Part C

1. Find the lowest D key on the keyboard.
2. From that key, play consecutive **minor 6ths** all the way across the keyboard.
3. Begin back down the same way, to the lowest D.

Part D

1. Find the lowest E♭ key on the keyboard.
2. From that key, play consecutive **minor 6ths** all the way across the keyboard.
3. Begin back down the same way, to the lowest E♭.

Random
1. Randomly pick a key on the keyboard and name it.
2. Play a minor 6th above and below the chosen key, naming each correctly.
3. Repeat steps 1 and 2 using many different keys.

KEYBOARD ACTIVITY #9

Part A
1. Find the lowest C key on the keyboard.
2. From that key, play consecutive **minor 7ths** all the way across the keyboard.
3. Begin back down the same way, to the lowest C.

Part B
1. Find the lowest D♭ key on the keyboard.
2. From that key, play consecutive **minor 7ths** all the way across the keyboard.
3. Begin back down the same way, to the lowest D♭.

Random
1. Randomly pick a key on the keyboard and name it.
2. Play a minor 7th above and below the chosen key, naming each correctly.
3. Repeat steps 1 and 2 using many different keys.

NOTE:
If you have not already done so, begin studying *scales*. Start with the *major scale*, where each note's distance from the starting key, or *tonic*, is either a major or perfect interval. Then proceed to the various types of *minor scales*, all of which contain the same perfect intervals as the major scale, yet each has its own "blend" of major and minor intervals. (Italicized terms can be found in the glossary). Perfect, major and minor intervals are common in most scales, unlike the remaining two interval qualities you will soon study.

Minor Interval Activity #4

Complete the following statements from memory, without looking at the keyboard.

1. A m3 above a G is _____.

2. A m7 below an A is _____.

3. A m2 above an E♭ is _____.

4. A m6 below a C is _____.

5. A m3 below an F♯ is _____.

6. A m7 above a D is _____.

7. A m2 below a B♭♭ is _____.

8. A m6 above an F is _____.

9. A m3 above an E♭ is _____.

10. A m7 below a G♭ is _____.

11. A m2 above a D♯ is _____.

12. A m6 below a G♭♭ is _____.

13. A m3 below a C is _____.

14. A m7 above an A♯ is _____.

15. A m2 below a D is _____.

16. A m6 above a C𝄪 is _____.

17. A m3 above an F♯ is _____.

18. A m7 below a D♭ is _____.

19. A m2 above an E is _____.

20. A m6 below a B♭ is _____.

EAR TRAINING ACTIVITY #3A

1. Listen to your partner play minor intervals melodically **up** from middle C in ascending order: m2, m3, m6, m7. Repeat until each interval is familiar.

2. Have your partner play minor intervals in random order while you name each aloud. Continue until you have correctly named at least 10 minor intervals in a row up from middle C.

3. Listen to minor intervals played melodically up from another key in ascending order: m2, m3, m6, m7. Repeat until each interval is familiar.

4. Have your partner play minor intervals in random order while you name each aloud. Continue until you have correctly named at least 10 minor intervals in a row up from the chosen key.

5. Repeat steps 3 and 4 on other keys, chosen by your partner, until you can correctly name every minor interval up from three different starting keys.

EAR TRAINING ACTIVITY #3B

1. Play a key near the bottom of your singing range. (This chosen key is played repeatedly throughout steps 2 and 3 to maintain pitch reference.)

2. Sing each of the four minor intervals **up** from the chosen pitch, in order: m2, m3, m6, m7. Sing both notes of each interval (the bottom pitch and the answer above). If you have trouble, play the upper key very briefly as a hint. Repeat this until you can correctly sing all four intervals at least twice through without reference to the keyboard.

3. Call out various minor intervals in random order, singing the notes of each interval aloud. Continue this until you can correctly sing 10 intervals in a row up from the same chosen pitch.

4. Repeat steps 1 - 3 using different lower-range keys until you can easily sing every minor interval up from three different starting keys.

EAR TRAINING ACTIVITY #3C

1. Listen to your partner play minor intervals melodically **down** from middle C in descending order: m2, m3, m6, m7. Repeat until each interval is familiar.

2. Have your partner play minor intervals in random order while you name each aloud. Continue until you have correctly named at least 10 minor intervals in a row down from middle C.

3. Listen to minor intervals played melodically down from another key in descending order: m2, m3, m6, m7. Repeat until each interval is familiar.

4. Have your partner play minor intervals in random order while you name each aloud. Continue until you have correctly named at least 10 minor intervals in a row down from the chosen key.

5. Repeat steps 3 and 4 on other keys, chosen by your partner, until you can correctly name every minor interval down from three different starting keys.

EAR TRAINING ACTIVITY #3D

1. Play a key near the top of your singing range. (This chosen key is played repeatedly throughout steps 2 and 3 to maintain pitch reference.)

2. Sing each of the four minor intervals **down** from the chosen pitch, in order: m2, m3, m6, m7. Sing both notes of each interval (the top pitch and the answer below). If you have trouble, play the lower key very briefly as a hint. Repeat this until you can correctly sing all four intervals at least twice through without reference to the keyboard.

3. Call out various minor intervals in random order, singing the notes of each interval aloud. Continue this until you can correctly sing 10 intervals in a row down from the same chosen pitch.

4. Repeat steps 1 - 3 using different upper-range keys until you can easily sing every minor interval down from three different starting keys.

MIXED INTERVAL ACTIVITY #1

Review the number of half steps for perfect, major, and minor intervals.
When you can recite them from memory, go on to Activity #2 below.

MIXED INTERVAL ACTIVITY #2

Write the correct interval name in each box below. Then play these intervals.
The first two are done as examples.

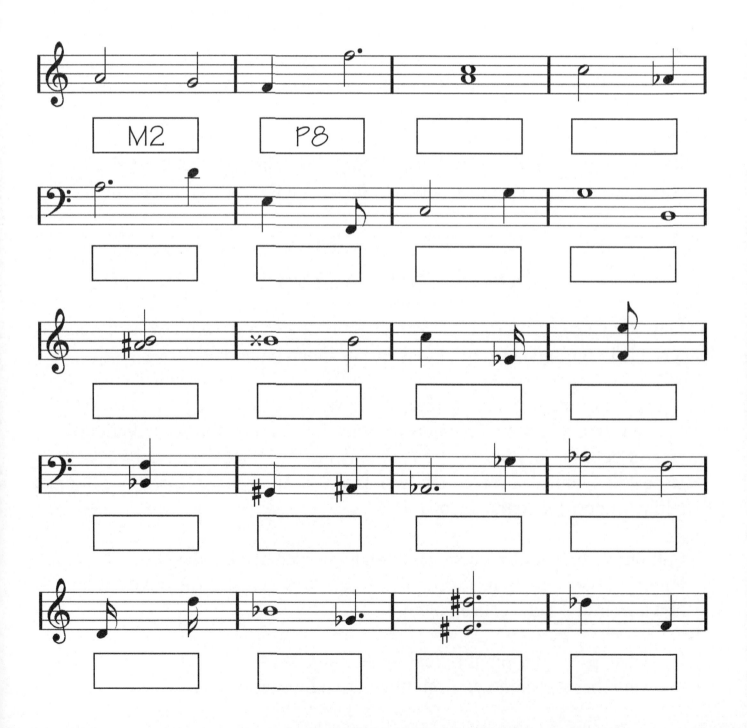

Mixed Interval Activity #3

1. Draw the harmonic interval **above** each note. Use the same notehead and a stem to make each interval into half notes. Remember the rules about stems.

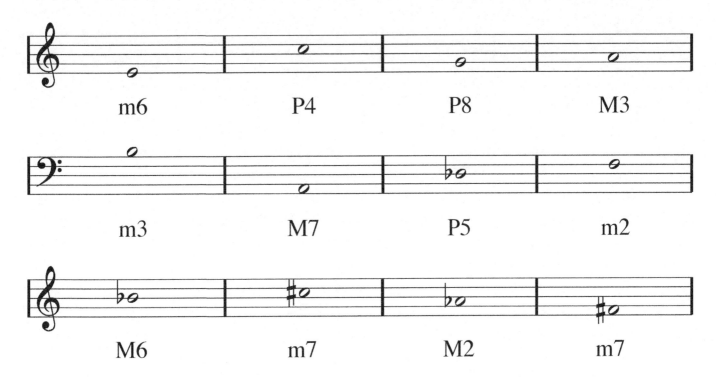

2. Draw the harmonic interval **below** each note making half note intervals as described above.

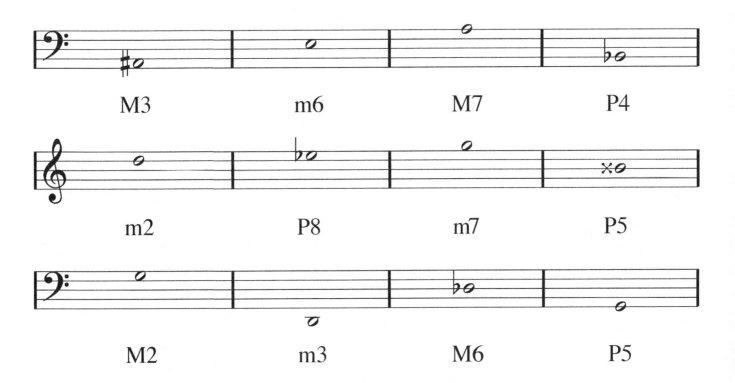

Mixed Interval Activity #4

1. Draw the melodic interval **above** each note. Then play these intervals.

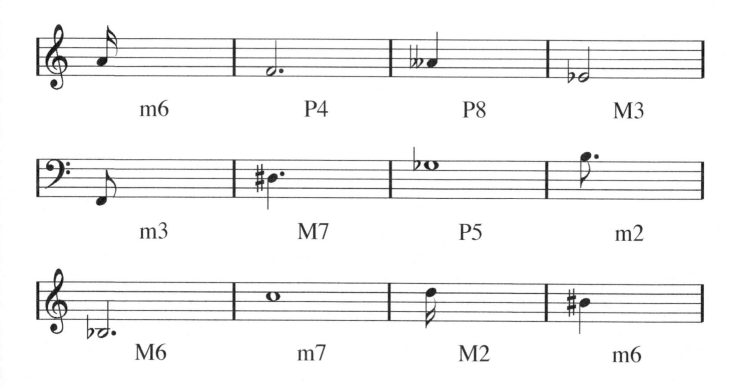

m6   P4   P8   M3

m3   M7   P5   m2

M6   m7   M2   m6

2. Draw the melodic interval **below** each note. Then play these intervals.

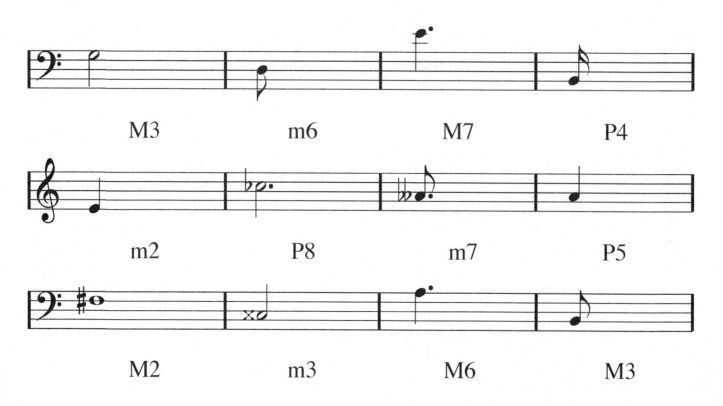

M3   m6   M7   P4

m2   P8   m7   P5

M2   m3   M6   M3

Mixed Interval Activity #5

Shade in the correct key **above and below** the keys with dots.

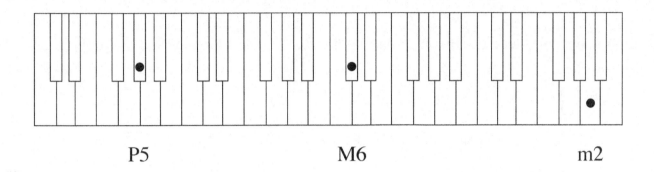

P5   M6   m2

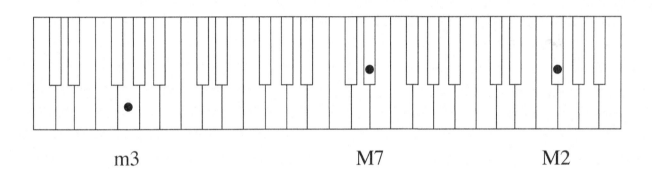

m3   M7   M2

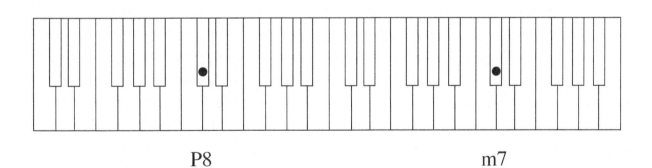

P8   m7

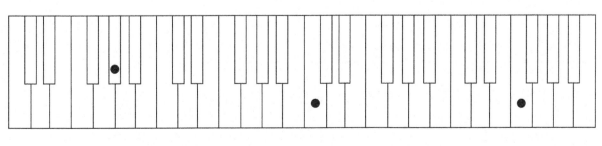

m6   M3   P4

Augmented Intervals

- Augmented intervals can be any number (unison - octave).
- Augmented intervals are **one half step greater** than major or perfect intervals.
- A capital "A" and the numbers 1 - 8 will represent this interval.

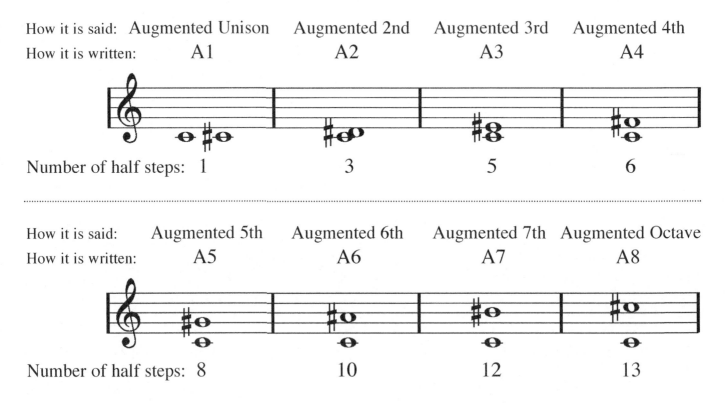

How it is said: Augmented Unison	Augmented 2nd	Augmented 3rd	Augmented 4th
How it is written: A1	A2	A3	A4

Number of half steps: 1   3   5   6

How it is said: Augmented 5th	Augmented 6th	Augmented 7th	Augmented Octave
How it is written: A5	A6	A7	A8

Number of half steps: 8   10   12   13

Notice that most of the half step numbers are the same as the minor and perfect intervals. For example, an Augmented 5th (A5) has the same number of half steps as a minor 6th, both having eight. Even though they have the same number of half steps, they are different intervals in both number and quality. The following examples clarify this point.

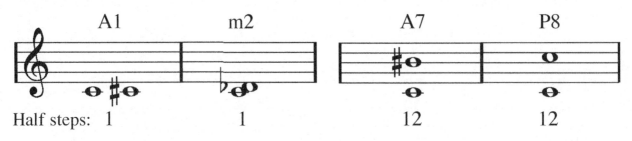

Half steps: 1   1   12   12

AUGMENTED INTERVAL ACTIVITY #1

Memorize the number of half steps for each of the eight augmented intervals above. When you can recite these without hesitation, go on to the next page.

Augmented Interval Activity #2

1. Draw the melodic interval an **A1 above** each note. Then play these.

2. Draw the melodic interval an **A1 below** each note. Then play these.

3. Draw the melodic interval an **A2 above** each note. Then play these.

4. Draw the melodic interval an **A2 below** each note. Then play these.

5. Draw the melodic interval an **A3 above** each note. Then play these.

6. Draw the melodic interval an **A3 below** each note. Then play these.

7. Draw the melodic interval an **A4 above** each note. Then play these.

8. Draw the melodic interval an **A4 below** each note. Then play these.

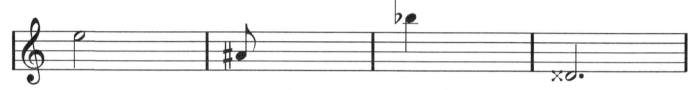

9. Draw the melodic interval an **A5 above** each note. Then play these.

10. Draw the melodic interval an **A5 below** each note. Then play these.

11. Draw the melodic interval an **A6 above** each note. Then play these.

12. Draw the melodic interval an **A6 below** each note. Then play these.

13. Draw the melodic interval an **A7 above** each note. Then play these.

14. Draw the melodic interval an **A7 below** each note. Then play these.

15. Draw the melodic interval an **A8 above** each note. Then play these.

16. Draw the melodic interval an **A8 below** each note. Then play these.

Augmented Interval Activity #3

Shade in the correct key **above and below** the keys with dots.

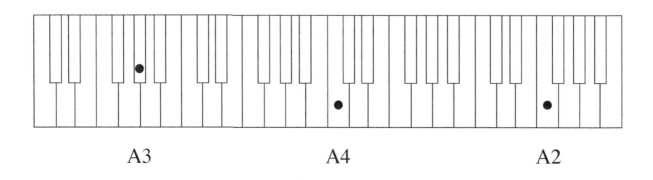

A3   A4   A2

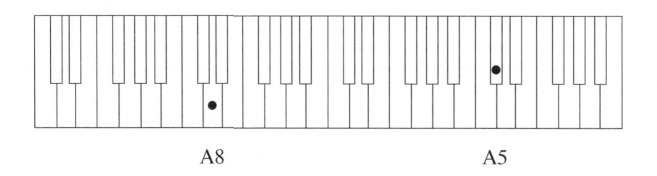

A8   A5

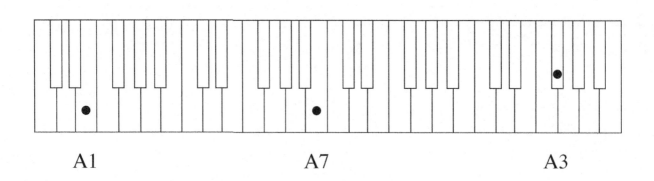

A1   A7   A3

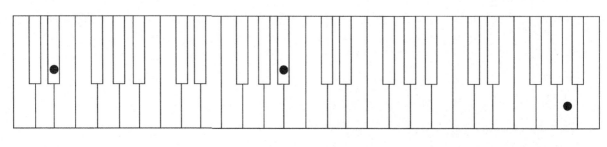

A2   A6   A1

NOTE:

Only the augmented 4th will be used in the following keyboard activity. It is the only interval within the perfect octave not yet played. All other augmented intervals have the same distance (half step number) as intervals already studied. The augmented octave is omitted in keyboard activities.

KEYBOARD ACTIVITY #10

Part A

1. Find the lowest C key on the keyboard.
2. From that key, play **augmented 4ths** all the way across the keyboard.
3. Begin back down the same way, to the lowest C.

Part B

1. Find the lowest D♭ key on the keyboard.
2. From that key, play **augmented 4ths** all the way across the keyboard.
3. Begin back down the same way, to the lowest D♭.

Part C

1. Find the lowest D key on the keyboard.
2. From that key, play **augmented 4ths** all the way across the keyboard.
3. Begin back down the same way, to the lowest D.

Part D

1. Find the lowest E♭ key on the keyboard.
2. From that key, play **augmented 4ths** all the way across the keyboard.
3. Begin back down the same way, to the lowest E♭.

Part E

1. Find the lowest E key on the keyboard.
2. From that key, play **augmented 4ths** all the way across the keyboard.
3. Begin back down the same way, to the lowest E.

Part F

1. Find the lowest F key on the keyboard.
2. From that key, play **augmented 4ths** all the way across the keyboard.
3. Begin back down the same way, to the lowest F.

Random

1. Randomly pick a key on the keyboard and name it.
2. Play an augmented 4th above and below the chosen key, naming each correctly.
3. Repeat steps 1 and 2 using many different keys.

Augmented Interval Activity #4

Complete the following statements from memory, without looking at the keyboard.

1. An A3 above an F is _____.

2. An A1 below an E is _____.

3. An A6 above a C♯ is _____.

4. An A8 below a G is _____.

5. An A5 above a D♭ is _____.

6. An A4 below a B is _____.

7. An A2 above a B♭ is _____.

8. An A7 below an A♯ is _____.

9. An A3 below a G is _____.

10. An A1 above an F♯ is _____.

11. An A6 below a D is _____.

12. An A8 above an A♭♭ is _____.

13. An A5 below an E♭ is _____.

14. An A4 above a C is _____.

15. An A2 below a C♯ is _____.

16. An A7 above an A♭ is _____.

17. An A1 above a D♭ is _____.

18. An A3 below an E♯ is _____.

19. An A6 above a C is _____.

20. An A4 below a C♯ is _____.

NOTE:

Only the augmented 4th will be used in the following ear training activities. It is the only interval within the perfect octave that has not been sung and is one of the most difficult to do so. All other augmented intervals have the same sound as those already studied. The augmented octave is omitted in ear training activities. Since the forthcoming *diminished* intervals also have the same sound and distances as previously studied intervals, ear training for both augmented and diminished qualities will be combined in Ear Training Activities #5A - 5D.

Tritone: Another name for the augmented 4th, so named because it is composed of three whole tones (whole steps). This interval exactly divides the perfect octave. Earlier in music history, its harsh sound was treated with much caution or avoidance. In late medieval times, it was regarded as the *diabolus in musica*, the "devil in music". By the 19th century, restrictions on its use were loosening and by the 20th century, new styles of music brought the tritone into widespread acceptance.

EAR TRAINING ACTIVITY #4A

1. Listen to your partner play the augmented 4th interval melodically **up and down** from middle C. Name the correct keys above and below middle C.
2. Have your partner play augmented 4ths melodically up and down from various starting keys. Your partner names the starting key and you correctly name the surrounding keys. Continue this until you have correctly named at least 20 keys in a row.

EAR TRAINING ACTIVITY #4B

1. Play a key near the middle of your singing range. (This chosen key is played repeatedly throughout step 2 to maintain pitch reference.)
2. Sing the chosen key and the augmented 4th **above and below** it. If you have trouble, play the answer very briefly as a hint. Repeat this until you can easily sing the chosen key and the augmented 4th above and below without reference to the keyboard.
3. Repeat steps 1 and 2 using different middle-range keys, until you can easily sing every chosen key and the augmented 4th above and below from five different starting keys in a row.

Diminished Intervals

- Diminished intervals can be any number except the unison.
- Diminished intervals are **one half step less** than minor or perfect intervals.
- A lower-case "d" and the numbers 2 - 8 will represent this interval.

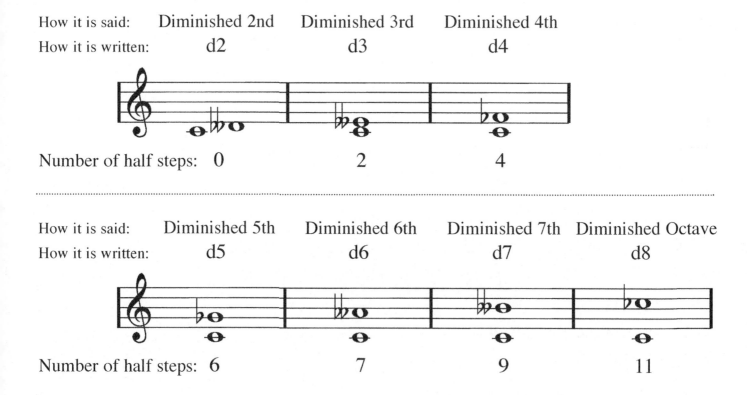

How it is said:	Diminished 2nd	Diminished 3rd	Diminished 4th
How it is written:	d2	d3	d4

Number of half steps: 0   2   4

How it is said:	Diminished 5th	Diminished 6th	Diminished 7th	Diminished Octave
How it is written:	d5	d6	d7	d8

Number of half steps: 6   7   9   11

Notice that many of the half step numbers are the same as the major and perfect intervals. For example, both the diminished 3rd (d3) and major 2nd have two half steps, yet they are different intervals in both number and quality. The same can be said of the perfect unison and the diminished 2nd, both having zero half steps. (The diminished unison does not exist because there cannot be less than zero half steps.)

DIMINISHED INTERVAL ACTIVITY #1

Memorize the number of half steps for each of the seven diminished intervals above. When you can recite these without hesitation, go on to the next page.

Diminished Interval Activity #2

1. Draw the melodic interval a **d2 above** each note. Then play these.

2. Draw the melodic interval a **d2 below** each note. Then play these.

3. Draw the melodic interval a **d3 above** each note. Then play these.

4. Draw the melodic interval a **d3 below** each note. Then play these.

5. Draw the melodic interval a **d4 above** each note. Then play these.

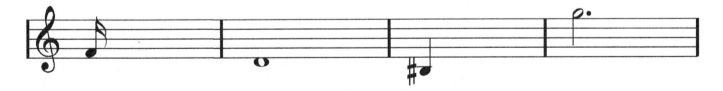

6. Draw the melodic interval a **d4 below** each note. Then play these.

7. Draw the melodic interval a **d5 above** each note. Then play these.

8. Draw the melodic interval a **d5 below** each note. Then play these.

9. Draw the melodic interval a **d6 above** each note. Then play these.

10. Draw the melodic interval a **d6 below** each note. Then play these.

11. Draw the melodic interval a **d7 above** each note. Then play these.

12. Draw the melodic interval a **d7 below** each note. Then play these.

13. Draw the melodic interval a **d8 above** each note. Then play these.

14. Draw the melodic interval a **d8 below** each note. Then play these.

Diminished Interval Activity #3

Shade in the correct key **above and below** the keys with dots. For the diminished 2nd, just shade in the correct key.

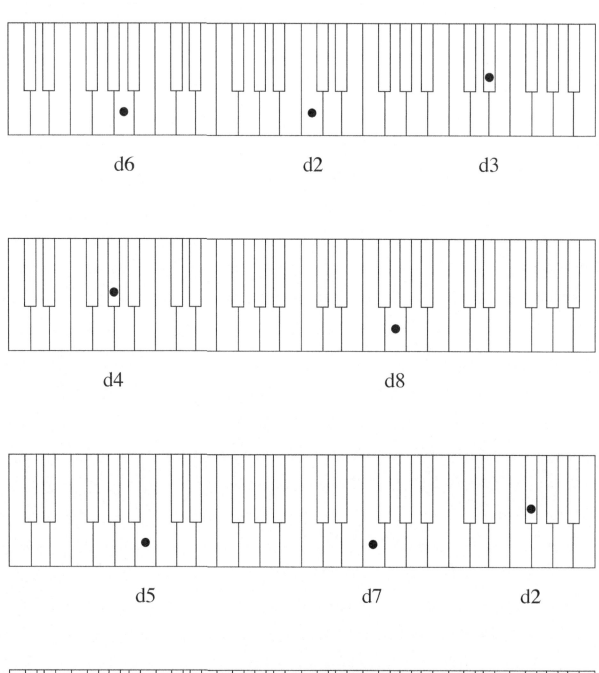

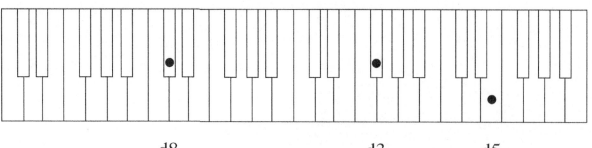

Diminished Interval Activity #4

Complete the following statements from memory, without looking at the keyboard.

1. A d2 above a G♯ is _____.

2. A d5 below an A is _____.

3. A d8 above a D is _____.

4. A d6 below a B♭ is _____.

5. A d3 above an F♯ is _____.

6. A d4 below a B is _____.

7. A d7 above a C is _____.

8. A d2 below a D♭♭ is _____.

9. A d5 above a G is _____.

10. A d8 below an F is _____.

11. A d6 above an E is _____.

12. A d3 below a C♯ is _____.

13. A d4 above a D♯ is _____.

14. A d7 below an A♭ is _____.

15. A d5 below a G♯ is _____.

16. A d8 above an E✕ is _____.

17. A d6 below an F is _____.

18. A d3 above a C is _____.

19. A d4 below a C♭♭ is _____.

20. A d7 above an F✕ is _____.

MIXED INTERVAL ACTIVITY #6

Review the number of half steps for augmented and diminished intervals.
When you can recite all of these from memory, go on to Activity #7 below.

MIXED INTERVAL ACTIVITY #7

Write the correct **augmented or diminished** interval name in each box below.
Then play these intervals.

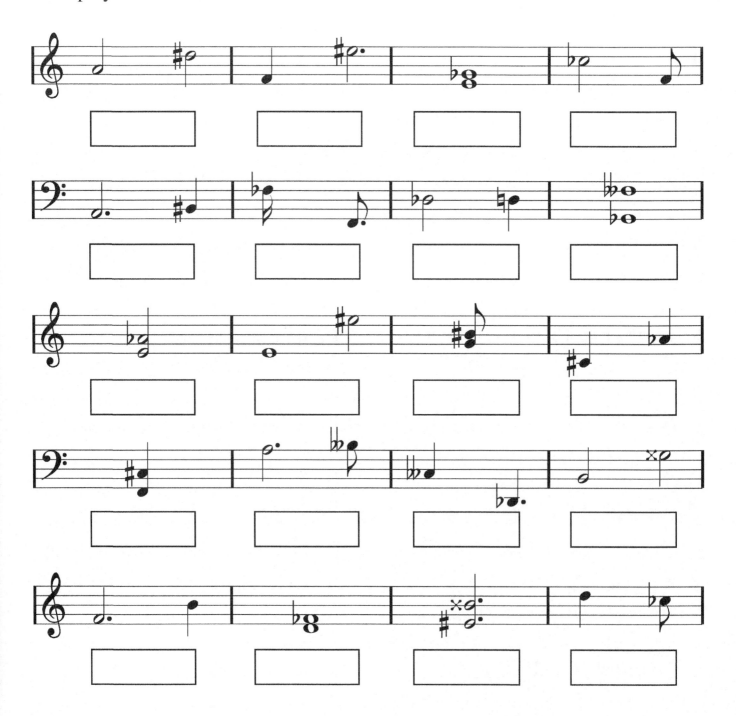

Mixed Interval Activity #8

1. Draw the harmonic interval **above** each note. Use the same notehead and a stem to make each interval into half notes. Remember the rules about stems.

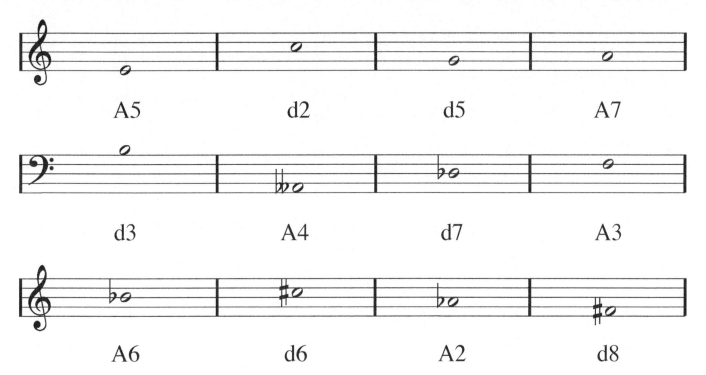

2. Draw the harmonic interval **below** each note making half note intervals as described above.

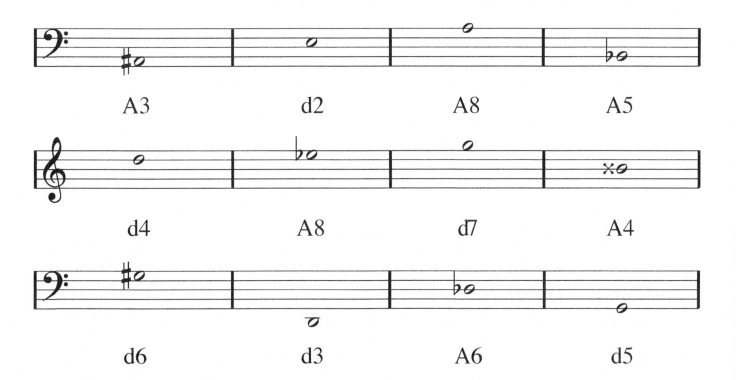

Mixed Interval Activity #9

Shade in the correct key **above and below** the keys with dots.

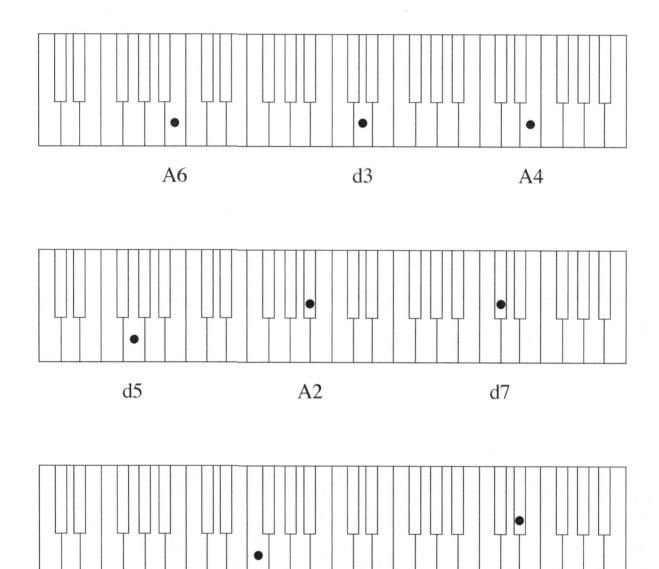

A6   d3   A4

d5   A2   d7

A8   d4

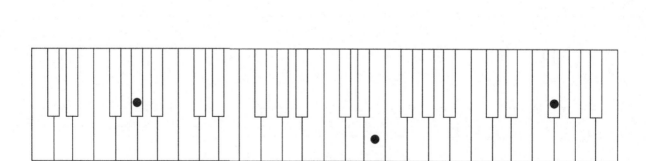

A5   d6   A1

NOTE: Omit the augmented octave (A8) from Ear Training Activities #5A - 5D.

EAR TRAINING ACTIVITY #5A

1. Listen to your partner play various intervals melodically **up** from middle C. Name each interval played as either **augmented or diminished**. Continue this until you have correctly named at least 10 intervals in a row.
2. Repeat step 1 on other keys, chosen by your partner, until you correctly name every augmented and diminished interval up from three different starting keys.

EAR TRAINING ACTIVITY #5B

1. Play a key near the bottom of your singing range and call out various **augmented and diminished** intervals. Sing both notes of each interval (the bottom pitch and the answer above). Continue this until you have correctly sung at least 10 augmented and diminished intervals in a row.
2. Repeat step 1 on other keys until you can easily sing every augmented and diminished interval up from three different starting keys.

EAR TRAINING ACTIVITY #5C

1. Listen to your partner play various intervals melodically **down** from middle C. Name each interval played as either **augmented or diminished**. Continue this until you have correctly named at least 10 intervals in a row.
2. Repeat step 1 on other keys, chosen by your partner, until you correctly name every augmented and diminished interval down from three different starting keys.

EAR TRAINING ACTIVITY #5D

1. Play a key near the top of your singing range and call out various **augmented and diminished** intervals. Sing both notes of each interval (the top pitch and the answer below). Continue this until you have correctly sung at least 10 augmented and diminished intervals in a row.
2. Repeat step 1 on other keys until you can easily sing every augmented and diminished interval down from three different starting keys.

Interval Review

Below are the intervals discussed so far. Notice the following:

1. There are at least three possible qualities for each interval number, with the exception of the unison which has only two.

| **Unisons:** | Augmented | - 1 half step |
| | Perfect | - 0 half steps |

2nds:	Augmented	- 3 half steps
	Major	- 2 half steps
	Minor	- 1 half step
	Diminished	- 0 half steps

3rds:	Augmented	- 5 half steps
	Major	- 4 half steps
	Minor	- 3 half steps
	Diminished	- 2 half steps

4ths:	Augmented	- 6 half steps
	Perfect	- 5 half steps
	Diminished	- 4 half steps

5ths:	Augmented	- 8 half steps
	Perfect	- 7 half steps
	Diminished	- 6 half steps

6ths:	Augmented	- 10 half steps
	Major	- 9 half steps
	Minor	- 8 half steps
	Diminished	- 7 half steps

7ths:	Augmented	- 12 half steps
	Major	- 11 half steps
	Minor	- 10 half steps
	Diminished	- 9 half steps

Octaves:	Augmented	- 13 half steps
	Perfect	- 12 half steps
	Diminished	- 11 half steps

2. There are two intervals for each half step quantity. Two intervals have 0 half steps, two intervals have 1 half step, two intervals have 2 half steps, etc.

Perfect Unison	**- 0 half steps**	Major 3rd	**- 4 half steps**
Diminished 2nd	**- 0 half steps**	Diminished 4th	**- 4 half steps**
Augmented Unison	**- 1 half step**	Augmented 3rd	**- 5 half steps**
Minor 2nd	**- 1 half step**	Perfect 4th	**- 5 half steps**
Major 2nd	**- 2 half steps**	Augmented 4th	**- 6 half steps**
Diminished 3rd	**- 2 half steps**	Diminished 5th	**- 6 half steps**
Augmented 2nd	**- 3 half steps**	Perfect 5th	**- 7 half steps**
Minor 3rd	**- 3 half steps**	Diminished 6th	**- 7 half steps**
			Etc.

In the following mixed interval activities, all five interval qualities will be used.

Mixed Interval Activity #10

Draw the harmonic interval **above** each note. Use the same notehead and a stem to make each interval into half notes. Then play these intervals.

Mixed Interval Activity #11

Draw the harmonic interval **below** each note. Use the same notehead and a stem to make each interval into half notes. Then play these intervals.

Mixed Interval Activity #12

Shade in the correct key **above and below** the keys with dots.

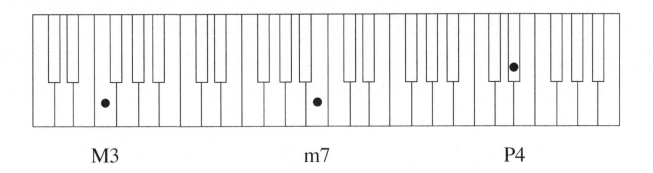

M3   m7   P4

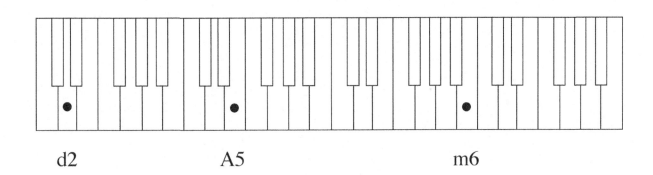

d2   A5   m6

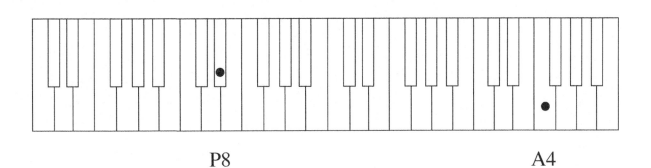

P8   A4

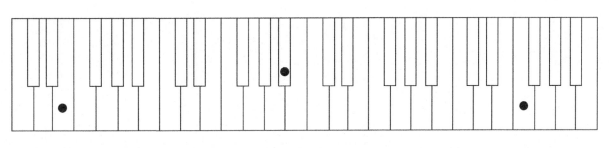

m3   M7   d4

Shade in the correct key **above and below** the keys with dots.

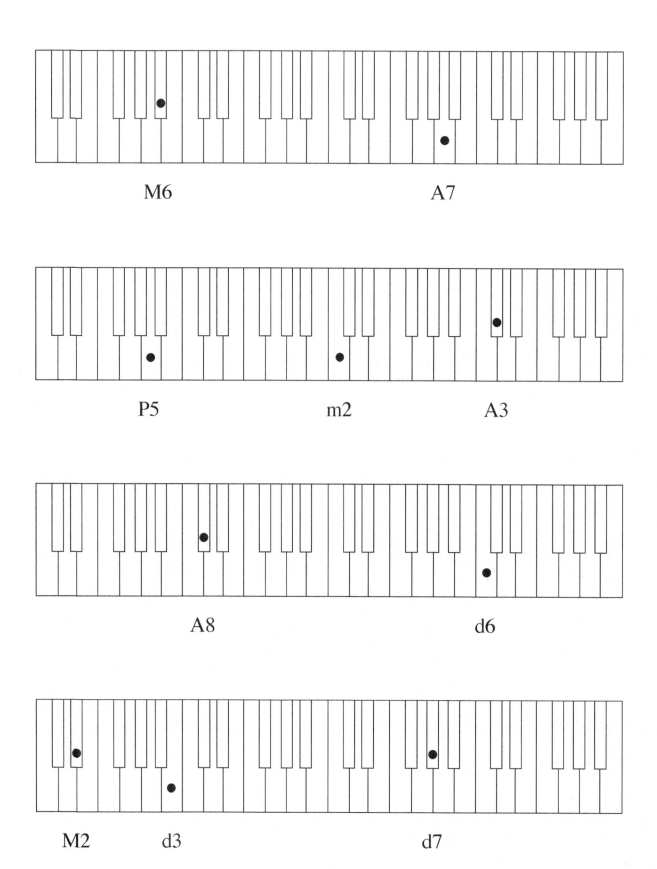

M6   A7

P5   m2   A3

A8   d6

M2   d3   d7

Mastering Intervals
Edition 3

Workshop 2 Checksheet

- *Consonant & Dissonant Intervals*
- *Enharmonics*
- *Harmonic Inversion*
- *Mirror Inversion*
- *Simple & Compound Intervals*
- *Compound Interval Inversion*

✓	**PROJECTS**
☐	1. Consonant & Dissonant Intervals and Activities #1 - 2
☐	2. Enharmonics and Activity #1
☐	3. Mixed Interval Final Exam
☐	4. Ear Training Activities #6A - 6D
☐	5. Harmonic Inversion and Activities #1 - 4
☐	6. Mirror Inversion and Activity #1
☐	7. Simple & Compound Intervals and Activities #1 - 3
☐	8. Compound Interval Inversion

Consonant & Dissonant Intervals

Consonance: Combinations of pitches that are considered pleasing to the ear. It can be considered that consonances do not sound as if they need to change or be resolved. A consonant interval sounds "stable" by itself.

Dissonance: Combinations of pitches that are considered displeasing to the ear. It can be considered that dissonances do sound as if they need to change or be resolved. A dissonant interval sounds "unstable" or "harsh" by itself.

1. **Consonant interval:** An interval (harmonic or melodic) that has consonance.
2. **Dissonant interval:** An interval (harmonic or melodic) that has dissonance.

- The following intervals are considered consonant:

Perfect Unison	Major 3rd	Major 6th
Perfect 4th	Minor 3rd	Minor 6th
Perfect 5th		
Perfect Octave		

- The following intervals are considered dissonant:

Major 2nd	Augmented 4th	Major 7th
Minor 2nd		Minor 7th

Dissonance is heard most easily in harmonic intervals, when the two pitches are simultaneous. Melody notes (which commonly move by 2nds) often do not sound dissonant against each other even though their distances can be labeled so.

CONSONANT & DISSONANT INTERVAL ACTIVITY #1

Memorize which intervals are consonant and which are dissonant. When you can recite these without hesitation, go on to Activity #2 below.

CONSONANT & DISSONANT INTERVAL ACTIVITY #2

Using middle C as the bottom note, play each of the consonant and dissonant intervals, harmonically, starting with the perfect unison and increasing by half steps up to the perfect octave. Listen to each interval carefully to develop an association between its sound and its label of consonant or dissonant.

Enharmonics

Enharmonic: Using a different name for the same pitch. For example, C♯ and D♭ are different names for the same pitch. When comparing these two note names to each other one could say that they are "enharmonically equivalent," or "enharmonically the same". Considering the double sharp and double flat possibilities, you will find that almost every pitch has three names. The examples below show different enharmonic situations.

Notice that the two notes in each measure are played on the same piano key. Can you see what the third pitch name would be for each of these examples?

Intervals can also be enharmonically the same. The interval number or quality does not have to remain the same, only the number of half steps. If the same number is used enharmonically, then the same quality must also be used. Each example on the first line below has the same interval name, whereas each example on the second line requires different names. Analyze each example.

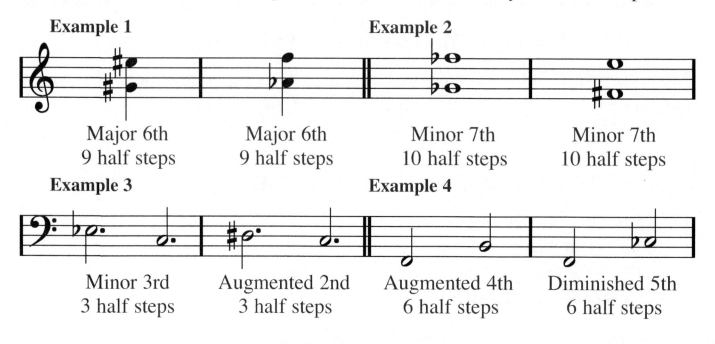

Enharmonic Interval Activity #1

Draw all enharmonic equivalents for the given interval. The structure for each answer is shown below the measure. The first interval is done as an example.

Mixed Interval Final Exam

For each interval on the keyboard, write out all possible enharmonic spellings along with their correct interval names. The first is done as an example.

- Move from the bottom key to the top key.
- Keep in mind all double sharp and double flat possibilities.
- The number of lines given indicates the number of possible answers.

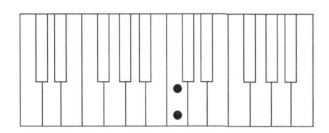

P1 = C to C
P1 = D♭♭ to D♭♭
P1 = B♯ to B♯
d2 = C to D♭♭
d2 = B♯ to C

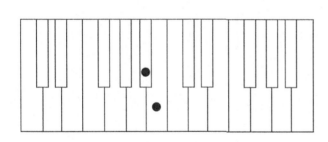

___ = ___ to ___
___ = ___ to ___
___ = ___ to ___
___ = ___ to ___
___ = ___ to ___

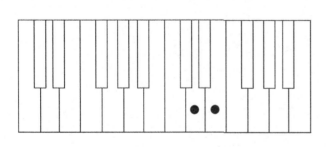

___ = ___ to ___
___ = ___ to ___
___ = ___ to ___
___ = ___ to ___
___ = ___ to ___

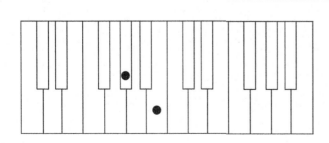

___ = ___ to ___
___ = ___ to ___
___ = ___ to ___
___ = ___ to ___

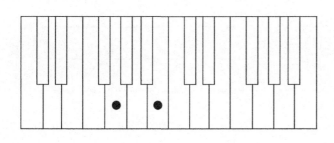

_____ = _____ to_____
_____ = _____ to_____
_____ = _____ to_____
_____ = _____ to_____
_____ = _____ to_____

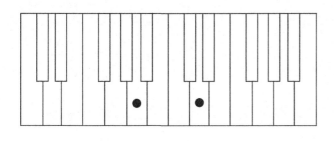

_____ = _____ to_____
_____ = _____ to_____
_____ = _____ to_____
_____ = _____ to_____
_____ = _____ to_____

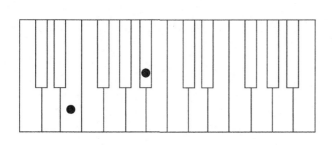

_____ = _____ to_____
_____ = _____ to_____
_____ = _____ to_____
_____ = _____ to_____
_____ = _____ to_____

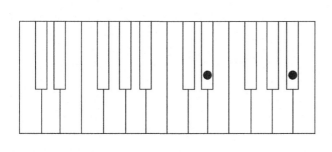

_____ = _____ to_____
_____ = _____ to_____
_____ = _____ to_____
_____ = _____ to_____
_____ = _____ to_____

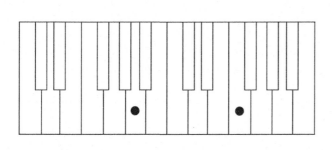

_____ = _____ to_____
_____ = _____ to_____
_____ = _____ to_____
_____ = _____ to_____
_____ = _____ to_____

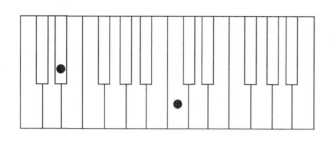

_____ = _____ to_____
_____ = _____ to_____
_____ = _____ to_____
_____ = _____ to_____
_____ = _____ to_____

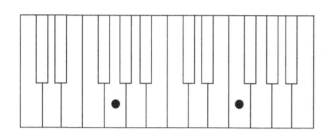

_____ = _____ to_____
_____ = _____ to_____
_____ = _____ to_____
_____ = _____ to_____
_____ = _____ to_____

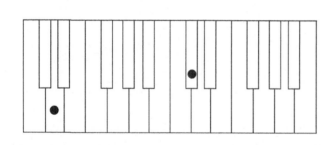

_____ = _____ to_____
_____ = _____ to_____
_____ = _____ to_____
_____ = _____ to_____
_____ = _____ to_____

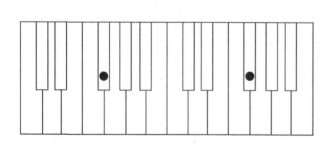

_____ = _____ to_____
_____ = _____ to_____
_____ = _____ to_____
_____ = _____ to_____
_____ = _____ to_____

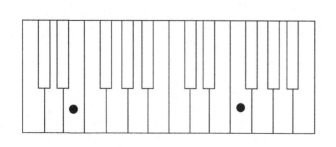

_____ = _____ to_____
_____ = _____ to_____

EAR TRAINING ACTIVITY #6A

1. Listen to your partner play various intervals melodically **up** from middle C. State the more common name for each interval (usually perfect, major, minor) and the two notes of each interval. Continue this until you have correctly named at least 10 intervals in a row.
2. Repeat step 1 on other keys, chosen by your partner, until you correctly name every interval and its keys, up from three different starting keys.

EAR TRAINING ACTIVITY #6B

1. Play a key near the bottom of your singing range and call out various intervals. Sing both notes of each interval (the bottom pitch and the answer above). Continue this until you have correctly sung at least 10 intervals in a row.
2. Repeat step 1 on other keys until you can easily sing every interval up from three different starting keys.

EAR TRAINING ACTIVITY #6C

1. Listen to your partner play various intervals melodically **down** from middle C. State the more common name for each interval (usually perfect, major, minor) and the two notes of each interval. Continue this until you have correctly named at least 10 intervals in a row.
2. Repeat step 1 on other keys, chosen by your partner, until you correctly name every interval and its keys, up from three different starting keys.

EAR TRAINING ACTIVITY #6D

1. Play a key near the top of your singing range and call out various intervals. Sing both notes of each interval (the top pitch and the answer below). Continue this until you have correctly sung at least 10 intervals in a row.
2. Repeat step 1 on other keys until you can easily sing every interval down from three different starting keys.

Harmonic Inversion

Harmonic inversion: Taking the bottom note of an interval and placing it in the next higher octave or taking the top note and placing it in the next lower octave. This produces a new interval. Any accidental is carried along with the inverted note. Here, "harmonic" has a different meaning since the concept of harmonic inversion can be applied to melodic intervals as well.

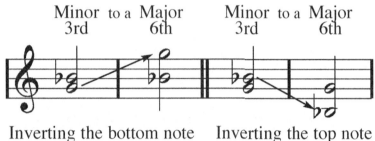

Minor to a Major
3rd   6th

Minor to a Major
3rd   6th

Inverting the bottom note
up one octave.

Inverting the top note
down one octave.

- Subtracting an interval from the number **9** will give you it's inversion number.

Examples:

The inversion of a 3rd is a 6th.
9 - 3 = 6

The inversion of a 5th is a 4th.
9 - 5 = 4

The inversion of a 7th is a 2nd.
9 - 7 = 2

Perfect to a Perfect
5th   4th

Perfect to a Perfect
5th   4th

Inverting the bottom note
up one octave.

Inverting the top note
down one octave.

Complement: Another name for the harmonic inversion of an interval. The name comes from the fact that an octave (P8) is formed when an interval and its complement are put together. Looking at the examples above, you can see how an octave is formed between the "arrow" notes.

Here are some other tips regarding harmonic inversion.

- Major intervals become minor.
- Minor intervals become major.
- Perfect intervals remain perfect.
- Augmented intervals become diminished.
- Diminished intervals become augmented.

HARMONIC INVERSION ACTIVITY #1

Memorize the following:

"9 minus the interval number equals the inversion number."

"When inverting intervals -
- major intervals become minor
- minor intervals become major
- perfect intervals remain perfect
- augmented intervals become diminished
- diminished intervals become augmented."

When you can recite these without hesitation, go on to Activity #2 below.

HARMONIC INVERSION ACTIVITY #2

Write the harmonic inversion for each interval below. Then play an example of each given interval along with its inversion.

1. m3 = _____   10. P1 = _____   19. P8 = _____

2. A7 = _____   11. A2 = _____   20. m6 = _____

3. P5 = _____   12. d5 = _____   21. M3 = _____

4. d8 = _____   13. m2 = _____   22. d7 = _____

5. A6 = _____   14. A3 = _____   23. A5 = _____

6. d6 = _____   15. M6 = _____   24. M7 = _____

7. P4 = _____   16. d4 = _____   25. A4 = _____

8. M2 = _____   17. A1 = _____   26. d3 = _____

9. d2 = _____   18. m7 = _____

Harmonic Inversion Activity #3

1. Draw the complement next to the given interval, inverting it **up**.
   Write the names of both intervals on the lines. Then play them.

2. Draw the complement next to the given interval, inverting it **down**.
   Write the names of both intervals on the lines. Then play them.

Harmonic Inversion Activity #4

For each keyboard below, do the following steps:

1. Shade in the key that is the indicated interval **above** the dotted key.
2. Shade in the key that is the **harmonic inversion below** the dotted key.
3. Name that inversion on the line provided, directly below the shaded key.

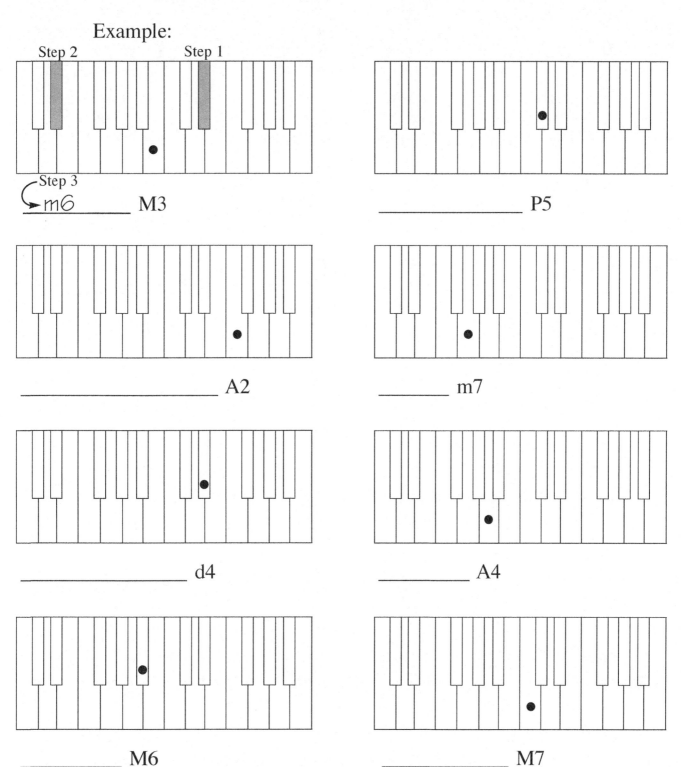

Example:

Step 2   Step 1

Step 3
m6 _____ M3

_____ P5

_____ A2

_____ m7

_____ d4

_____ A4

_____ M6

_____ M7

Mirror Inversion

Mirror inversion: An inversion having the same number of half steps as the original interval. It is also called **strict inversion** or **real inversion**.

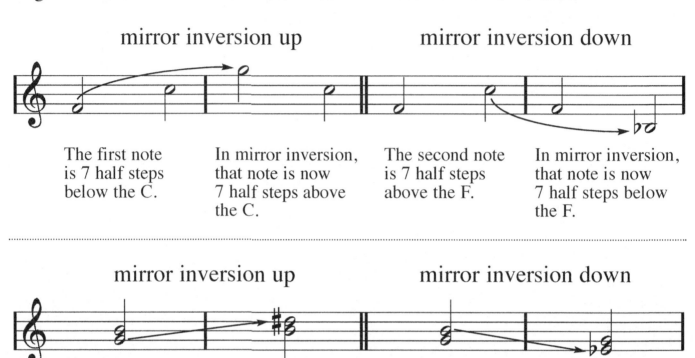

mirror inversion up   mirror inversion down

| The first note is 7 half steps below the C. | In mirror inversion, that note is now 7 half steps above the C. | The second note is 7 half steps above the F. | In mirror inversion, that note is now 7 half steps below the F. |

mirror inversion up   mirror inversion down

| The bottom note is 4 half steps below the B. | In mirror inversion, that note is now 4 half steps above the B. | The top note is 4 half steps above the G. | In mirror inversion, that note is now 4 half steps below the G. |

- The mirror inversions on the first line above, produced the same interval names as the originals, all being perfect 5ths. The same can be said of the second line, which resulted only in major 3rds. However, mirror inversion does not require the same interval name as the original. Though the distance must remain identical to the original interval, enharmonic equivalents can be used. Mirror-inverting the second interval on the next page (E up to C♭), upward, produces five enharmonic possibilities: C♭ to G♭ (P5), B to G♭ (d6), B to F♯ (P5), A✕ to F♯ (d6), or A✕ to E✕ (P5). Keeping C♭ as the bottom note in the inversion gives you the more appropriate answer, C♭ to G♭, a perfect 5th instead of the original diminished 6th. **The best answer is one which keeps the "pivot" note the same name.**

- Because the augmented 4th divides the octave (P8) in half, it is the only interval whose mirror inversion and harmonic inversion are identical in distance.

Mirror Inversion Activity #1

1. Draw the mirror inversion next to each interval below, inverting it **up**.
   Enharmonic equivalents may be used, but keep the pivot note the same.

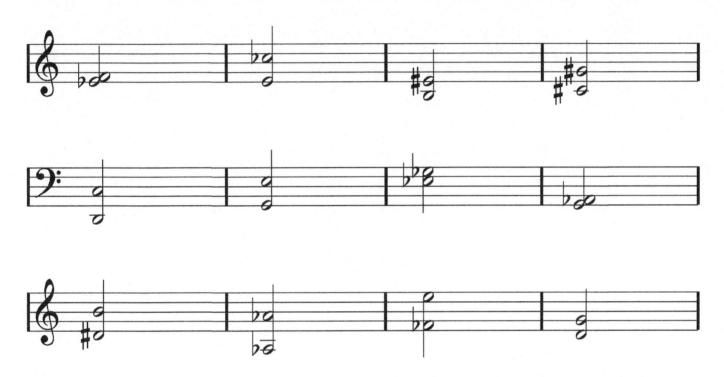

2. Draw the mirror inversion next to each interval below, inverting it **down**.
   Enharmonic equivalents may be used, but keep the pivot note the same.

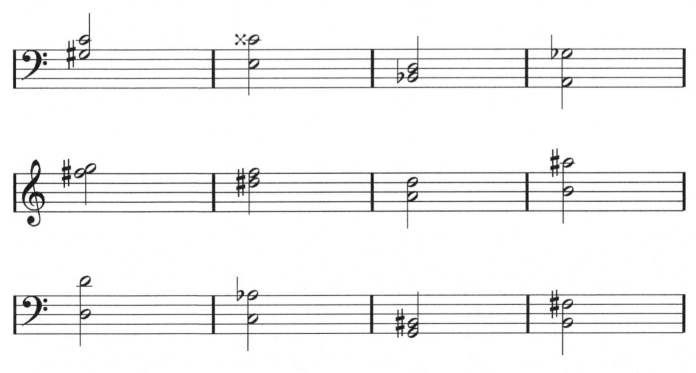

Simple & Compound Intervals

1. **Simple interval:** One octave or smaller in size; unisons through octaves.
2. **Compound interval:** Larger than an octave; typically 9ths through 15ths.

Here are the simple and compound intervals of the C Major scale.

SIMPLE INTERVALS

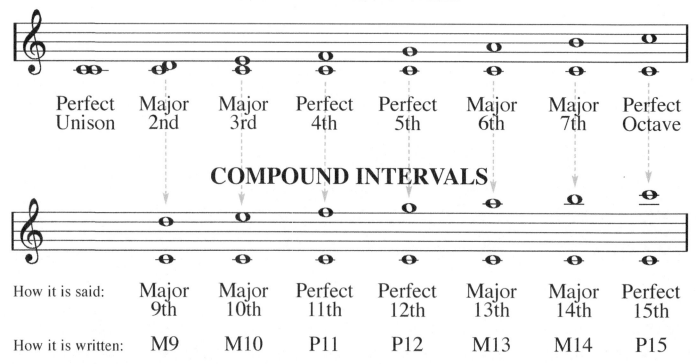

| Perfect
Unison | Major
2nd | Major
3rd | Perfect
4th | Perfect
5th | Major
6th | Major
7th | Perfect
Octave |

COMPOUND INTERVALS

How it is said:	Major 9th	Major 10th	Perfect 11th	Perfect 12th	Major 13th	Major 14th	Perfect 15th
How it is written:	M9	M10	P11	P12	M13	M14	P15

- Compound intervals can be thought of as an octave (P8) plus a simple interval.
  Examples: A major 9th is the same as an octave plus a major 2nd.
            A perfect 11th is the same as an octave plus a perfect 4th.

- Compound intervals have the same qualities as their related simple intervals.
  Examples: A 10th can be major, minor, augmented, or diminished, like the 3rd.
            A 12th can be perfect, augmented, or diminished, like the 5th.

- Subtracting the number **7** from a compound interval will give you its related simple interval number.
  Examples: Perfect 11th - 7 = perfect 4th. Major 13th - 7 = major 6th.

- Adding **7** to a simple interval will give you its related compound interval.
  Examples: Perfect 4th + 7 = perfect 11th. Major 6th + 7 = major 13th.

Compound Interval Activity #1

1. Write the related simple interval for each compound interval below.

1. d9 = _____	9. A12 = _____	17. M14 = _____
2. P12 = _____	10. d14 = _____	18. A13 = _____
3. M13 = _____	11. A10 = _____	19. m10 = _____
4. A11 = _____	12. d11 = _____	20. P11 = _____
5. m14 = _____	13. A15 = _____	21. d12 = _____
6. M10 = _____	14. M9 = _____	22. A9 = _____
7. P15 = _____	15. A14 = _____	23. m9 = _____
8. m13 = _____	16. d15 = _____	24. d10 = _____

2. Write the related compound interval for each simple interval below.

1. m3 = _____	9. d2 = _____	17. P8 = _____
2. A7 = _____	10. m7 = _____	18. m6 = _____
3. P5 = _____	11. d5 = _____	19. M3 = _____
4. M2 = _____	12. m2 = _____	20. d7 = _____
5. A6 = _____	13. A3 = _____	21. A5 = _____
6. d6 = _____	14. M6 = _____	22. M7 = _____
7. P4 = _____	15. d4 = _____	23. A4 = _____
8. A8 = _____	16. A2 = _____	24. d3 = _____

Compound Interval Activity #2

1. Draw the related **compound** interval next to each simple interval below.
   Write the names of both intervals on the lines. Then play them.

2. Draw the related **simple** interval next to each compound interval below.
   Write the names of both intervals on the lines. Then play them.

NOTE:

Ear training with compound intervals may now be studied, if so desired. Substitute each simple interval given in the previous ear training activities with the related compound interval, i.e., M9 instead of M2, P11 instead of P4, etc.

Compound Interval Activity #3

Complete the following statements from memory, without looking at the keyboard. Subtract the number **7** from the interval number to make the answer easier to find. After completing all answers, play each compound interval on the keyboard.

1. A M10 above a G is _____.

2. A d12 below an A is _____.

3. A m14 above a D is _____.

4. A d9 below a B♭ is _____.

5. A P12 above an F♯ is _____.

6. An A13 below a B is _____.

7. A M9 above a C is _____.

8. A m10 below a D♭♭ is _____.

9. A P15 above a G is _____.

10. An A11 below an F is _____.

11. A d14 above an E is _____.

12. A M13 below a C♯ is _____.

13. A m13 above a D♯ is _____.

14. An A9 below an A♭ is _____.

15. A d10 below a G♯ is _____.

16. A M14 above an A is _____.

17. A d11 below a B is _____.

18. An A15 above a C is _____.

19. A m9 below a G is _____.

20. A P11 above an E is _____.

Compound Interval Inversion

1. HARMONIC INVERSION

Compound intervals function the same as their related simple intervals, so they are usually reduced to simple intervals for the purpose of analysis. As a result, compound intervals are not widely used in music theory. However, inverting compound intervals merits some discussion.

The most important concept of inversion to remember is that one of the notes must be "flipped". In other words, the bottom note must be moved **above** the top note or vice-versa, otherwise there is no inversion. Measure 1, below, is the compound interval of a minor 10th. We will now move the low A up in octaves.

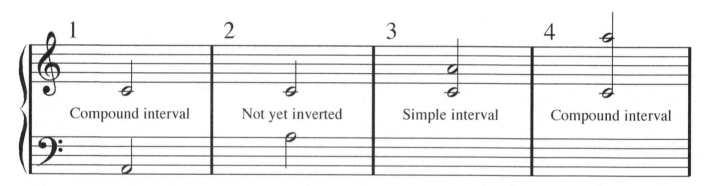

In measure 2, the lower A is shifted to "the next higher octave" per the definition of *harmonic inversion* on page 76, yet no inversion has taken place because the A is not yet above the middle C.

In measure 3, inversion has now occurred because the A is now above middle C. This inversion resulted in a simple interval. We could call it *harmonic* inversion since the upper note has the same name as the low A we started with, but it is not a *complement*.

In measure 4, the A is taken one octave higher to yield a compound interval. This "compound inversion" may or may not be considered the true inversion of the original minor 10th. There is no convention on this issue. Therefore, use the following two principles:
1. Simple intervals, when harmonically inverted, remain simple.
2. Compound intervals, when harmonically inverted, can become simple or compound.

2. MIRROR INVERSION

Since mirror inversion must retain the same distance as the original interval, the inversion process for compound intervals is conceptually easier and very exact. The examples below demonstrate the mirror inversion of two compound intervals.

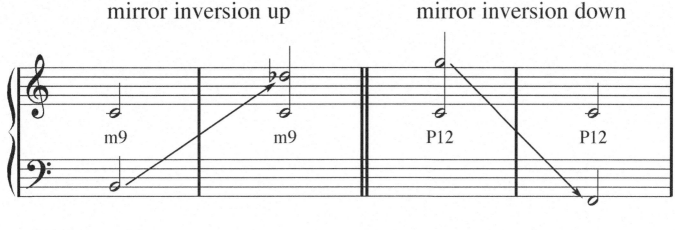

The bottom note is 13 half steps below the C.	In mirror inversion, that note is now 13 half steps above the C.	The top note is 19 half steps above the C.	In mirror inversion, that note is now 19 half steps below the C.

In the first example, the interval of a m9 is preserved when inverted in the second measure. In the second example, the interval of a P12 is also preserved when inverted in the fourth measure.

From these examples, we can safely assume that mirror-inverting any compound interval will always result in a compound inversion, since the half step quantity is retained. Mirror-inverting any simple interval will always result in a simple inversion, for the same reason.

Now we have two additional principles:

1. Simple intervals, when mirror-inverted, remain simple.
2. Compound intervals, when mirror-inverted, remain compound.

Reducing the previous information, we now have three final principles:

1. Simple intervals, when inverted by either method, remain simple.

2. Compound intervals, when mirror-inverted, remain compound.

3. Compound intervals, when harmonically inverted, can become simple or compound.

Mastering Intervals
Edition 3

Workshop 3 Checksheet

• *Music Analyses*

✓	**PROJECTS**
☐	1. Music Analysis Activity Guide
☐	2. Music Analysis Activity #1 - Couperin
☐	3. Music Analysis Activity #2 - Bach
☐	4. Music Analysis Activity #3 - Bach
☐	5. Music Analysis Activity #4 - Mozart
☐	6. Music Analysis Activity #5 - Haydn
☐	7. Music Analysis Activity #6 - Schumann
☐	8. Music Analysis Activity #7 - Chopin
☐	9. Music Analysis Activity #8 - Wehrli
☐	10. Music Analysis Activity #9 - Liszt
☐	11. Music Analysis Activity #10 - Ravel
☐	12. Music Analysis Activity #11 - Bartok
☐	13. Music Analysis Activity #12 - Poulenc
☐	14. Music Analysis Activity #13 - Webern
☐	15. Music Analysis Activity #14 - Evans
☐	16. Music Analysis Activity #15 - Corea

Music Analysis Activity Guide

In this workshop, fifteen music excerpts will be analyzed for intervallic content. A variety of other music-theory concepts and structures will also be presented. These excerpts are loosely arranged in stylistic order, showing some of the changes in melodic and harmonic style over the past three centuries. The title, composer and composition date are given for each excerpt. Where the composition date is unavailable, the birth and death dates of the composer are given.

PROCEDURE

- Do the steps of each activity in the order given. Do not skip any steps.
- Print all answers **clearly**, fitting on the lines provided.
- Note the key signature and accidentals in order to correctly name each interval.

- The last step in each music analysis activity is to play the excerpt repeatedly, each time thinking of one of the discoveries made in that activity. This step helps you (1) correlate the presented theory with the resulting sound, (2) discover the aesthetics of the style and (3) develop recognition of the style. (Answers should be checked in the **Answer Manual** before starting this step.)
- Fingering is omitted for space considerations, but should be worked out before practicing any excerpt hands together.
- If a tempo mark is given, try to achieve that speed. If the tempo is beyond your ability level, play it slower or perhaps with a smaller note value getting each beat. For example, the excerpt for Music Analysis Activity #2 can be played using the sixteenth note as each beat, giving the 64th notes an easier 16th note feel.
- Pedaling may be included where appropriate.

- After completing these activities, continue to analyze the intervals in music you encounter, asking yourself these two questions:
"What thoughts or feelings does this music evoke?"
"What interval groups or patterns contribute to those thoughts or feelings?"

Music Analysis Activity #1

1. Name each melodic interval in the upper staff. The first two intervals are given as examples.
2. Name each melodic interval in the lower staff. The first two intervals are given as examples.

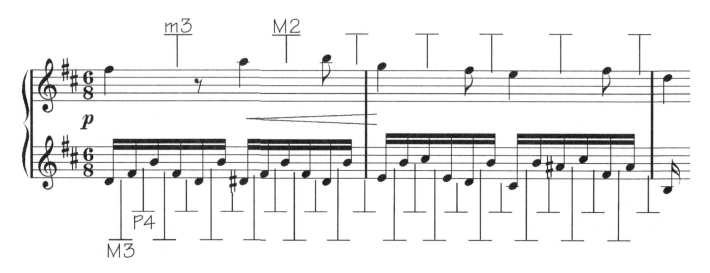

Les Rozeaux by Francois Couperin (1668 - 1733).

3. What are the only two interval numbers used in the upper-staff melody?
   _____ _____ These are the two most frequent intervals in musical melodies. Their melodic distances are agreeable to the ear and they often clarify what key or scale a work is based upon.
4. Notice the variety of melodic intervals in the lower staff.
5. Notice that the lower-staff notes form harmonic intervals with the upper notes.
6. Although harmonic texture is created between the lines, their horizontal movement as separate lines is the hallmark of this style of composition.
   Counterpoint: Note against note; music having two or more melodic lines that sound simultaneously. One line predominates over the others yet each retains its character as a line. This was the main form of composition between about 1650 and 1750.
7. A. Play the upper staff, thinking of the discovery in step 3.
   B. Play the lower staff, thinking of the discovery in step 4.
   C. Play hands together, thinking of the discoveries in steps 5 - 6.
   D. What thoughts or feelings does this music evoke?

Music Analysis Activity #2

1. Name each melodic interval in the treble staff.

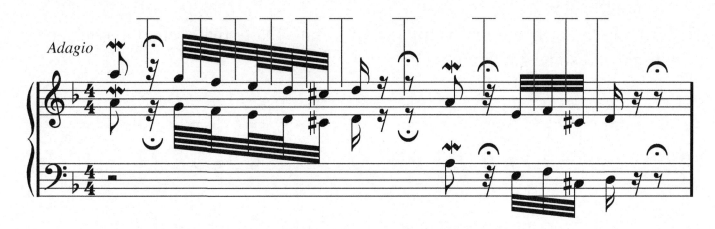

Toccata & Fugue in D Minor, BWV 565 by Johann Sebastian Bach. Composed circa 1709.

2. What are the only two interval numbers in this melody? _____ _____
3. Notice the mordent symbols (✹) on beats 1 and 3.
   Mordent: A quick melodic movement from the principal note (shown), down a diatonic step and back up. This movement produced what interval? _____
4. What is the interval from the first eighth note to the first sixteenth? _____
   What is the interval from the second eighth to the second sixteenth? _____
5. Each of the two melodic phrases ends a perfect 5th away from where it began. The second phrase is a variation of the first, stated a perfect octave lower.
6. Play the two intervals from step 4. How do they sound, one after the other? Plain? The mordents that begin each perfect 5th plus the notes within each 5th add tremendously to what would have otherwise been a stark and very unimaginative melody.
7. The right-hand melody is not being supported by accompaniment in the left hand, as it was in the Couperin excerpt. Instead, the left hand reinforces the melody by playing the same notes an octave (P8) below.
8. A. Play the right hand, thinking of the discoveries in steps 2 - 6.
   B. Play the left hand.
   C. Play hands together, thinking of the discovery in step 7.
   D. What thoughts or feelings does this music evoke?

Music Analysis Activity #3

1. Name each harmonic interval in the treble staff. At the circled notes, keep in mind that a preceding quarter note is overlapping and therefore creating a harmonic interval.
2. Name each harmonic interval in the bass staff. Note that some intervals are simple and some are compound.

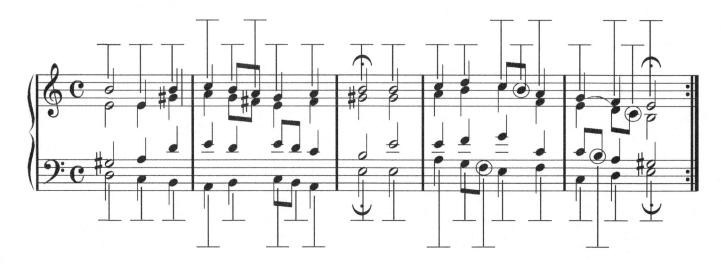

Chorale #10, *Aus tiefer Not schrei' ich zu dir* by Johann Sebastian Bach (1685 - 1750).

3. The most prevalent (frequently occurring) interval in the treble staff is the _____.
4. The most prevalent compound interval in the bass staff is the_____.
5. This excerpt is a 4-voice chorale written on the grand staff, intended to be sung by a choir or vocal ensemble. Each voice is distinguished in name and appearance.
   Soprano: The higher treble-staff voice with stems upward.
   Alto: The lower treble-staff voice with stems downward.
   Tenor: The higher bass-staff voice with stems upward.
   Bass: The lower bass-staff voice with stems downward.
   Stem direction clarifies the separation of voices.
6. Notice the circled B in the fourth measure of the treble staff. Here, the soprano voice momentarily crosses below the alto voice.
7. A. Play the treble staff, thinking of the discovery in step 3.
   B. Play the bass staff, thinking of the discovery in step 4. Use the right hand for the tenor voice, due to compound intervals.
   C. Play hands together, thinking of the discovery in step 5. Use the right hand for the tenor voice, as needed.
   D. What thoughts or feelings does this music evoke?

Music Analysis Activity #4

1. Name each melodic interval in the upper staff, through measure 2.
2. Name the five harmonic intervals in the upper staff.
3. Name each harmonic interval in the lower staff.

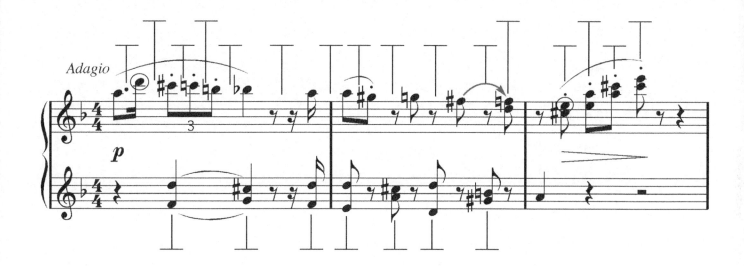

Fantasia I in D Minor by Wolfgang Amadeus Mozart (1756 - 1791).

4. The most prevalent interval in the melody is the _____.
5. Read the melody from the first circled note to the second. Mozart made this long series of descending minor 2nds interesting by using various rhythms as well as supporting harmonic intervals which, along with the melody, clarify the harmony of this passage.
6. Notice how the harmonic intervals in the lower staff alternate in width. Particularly in the second measure, this gives the accompaniment the feeling of expanding and contracting against the descending melody.
7. Considering the discovery in step 6, what do you think the accompaniment would sound like if we inverted the intervals down? Try it as part of step 8B.
8. A. Play the upper staff, thinking of the discoveries in steps 4 - 5.
   B. Play the lower staff, thinking of the discoveries in steps 6 - 7.
   C. Play hands together.
   D. What thoughts or feelings does this music evoke?

Music Analysis Activity #5

1. Name the indicated melodic intervals in the treble staff.
2. Below the bass staff, name the harmonic intervals created by crossing the two staves.

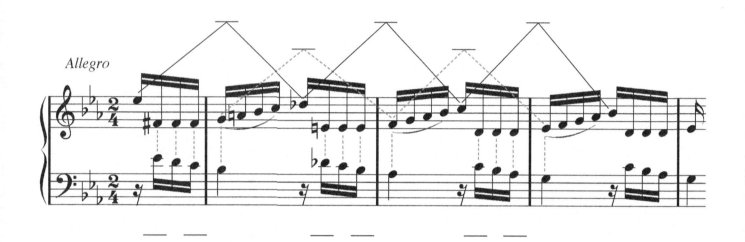

Piano Sonata #18 in Eb Major by Franz Joseph Haydn (1732 - 1809).

3. On beat 1 of each full measure, the melody in the treble staff drops by what interval? _____ On beat 2 of each measure, the melody in the treble staff drops by what two types of intervals? _____ _____

4. Do you notice patterns in the melody and left-hand accompaniment?
   The patterns are two beats in length and move down by steps (M2 or m2).
   Sequence: Repeating a musical phrase at a different pitch, typically a 2nd or 3rd away (though any distance can be used).
   Melodic sequence: Repetition in the melody only, as described above.
   Harmonic sequence: Similar repetition in other parts, along with the melody.

5. The harmonic sequence above is revealed, in part, by harmonic intervals which are spreading apart by nearly the same distances in each repetition.

6. A. Play the treble staff, thinking of the discoveries in steps 3 - 4.
   B. Play the bass staff, thinking of the discovery in step 4.
   C. Play hands together, thinking of the discoveries in steps 4 - 5.
   D. What thoughts or feelings does this music evoke?

Music Analysis Activity #6

1. Name the indicated melodic intervals in the upper staff.
2. Name the indicated harmonic intervals in the lower staff. For groups of three notes, put the interval between the top two notes on the upper line and the interval between the bottom two notes on the lower line. The first is given as an example.

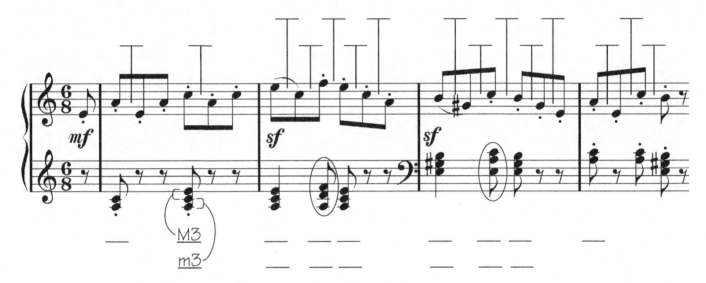

Wilder Reiter, Album for the Young, Opus 68, #8 by Robert Schumann. Composed in 1848.

3. Notice the sequence in the upper staff, third measure. This repeated phrase from the second measure drops by what interval? _____
4. The accompaniment also drops at the same time by what amount? _____
   The third measure demonstrates what type of sequence? _____
5. The stacked harmonic intervals in the lower staff create *chords*. Chords are most commonly made up of stacked thirds, as shown above.
6. Look at the circled chords. If we harmonically invert the top two notes below the bottom note, the resulting chords are stacked thirds, like the others.
   Chords can be harmonically inverted, just like intervals.
7. A. Play the upper staff, thinking of the discovery in step 3.
   B. Play the lower staff, thinking of the discoveries in steps 4 - 6.
   C. Play hands together.
   D. What thoughts or feelings does this music evoke?

Music Analysis Activity #7

1. Name each melodic interval in the treble staff.
2. Name the harmonic intervals within each chord of the bass staff.
   Put the interval between the top two notes on the upper line and the interval between the bottom two notes on the lower line.

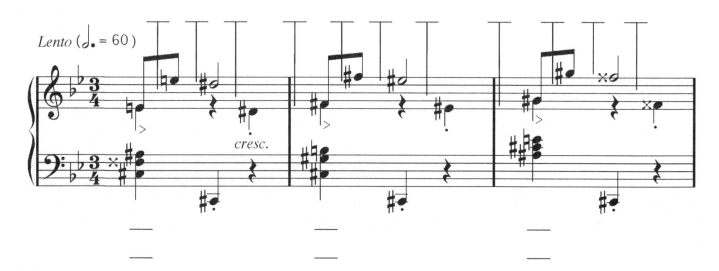

Nocturne in G Minor, Opus 15, #3 by Frederic Chopin. Composed in 1834.

3. Notice the sequence in the treble-staff melody. From measure to measure, this melodic sequence is shifting up by what interval? _____
4. In each repetition, these melodic intervals are exactly the same.
   Real sequence: Each repetition contains exactly the same intervals as the first statement. (**Tonal** or **diatonic sequence:** Each repetition remains in the same key as the first statement. In order to stay in one key, some of the interval distances would have to change by half steps.)
5. The most prevalent interval in the bass-staff chords is the _____.
   These chords have structures similar to those in the Schumann excerpt.
   Looking at the first chord, if we invert the top two notes down (or the bottom one up) the resulting chord is made up of stacked _____.
6. A. Play the treble staff, thinking of the discoveries in steps 3 - 4.
   B. Play the bass staff, thinking of the discovery in step 5.
   C. Play hands together.
   D. What thoughts or feelings does this music evoke?

Music Analysis Activity #8

1. Name each melodic interval in the treble staff.
2. Below the bass staff, name the simple and compound harmonic intervals created across the two staves. Omit the circled interval until step 6.

Prelude 5 by Barry Michael Wehrli. Composed in 2002.

3. The most prevalent interval number in the treble staff is the _____.
4. Although the right-hand melody sounds like a sequence, it is not, due to the changing interval pattern in each measure.
5. Looking at the melodic intervals in the bass staff, what is the most prevalent interval number? _____
6. The circled interval is larger than a 15th, but not by much. Even though it is an "extended" compound interval, name it correctly, using the compound interval theory already learned. The harmonic intervals on the first beat of each measure could also be determined this way.
7. Notice the variety of compound intervals between the right and left hands.
8. Notice that the two melodic lines are usually moving in opposite directions.
   Contrary motion: a. Two voices moving in opposite directions.
   b. Harmonic intervals whose notes move away from or towards each other.
9. A. Play the treble staff, thinking of the discoveries in step 3 - 4.
   B. Play the bass staff, thinking of the discovery in step 5.
   C. Play hands together, thinking of the discoveries in steps 6 - 8.
   D. What thoughts or feelings does this music evoke?

Music Analysis Activity #9

1. In section A, name the 5 melodic intervals in the soprano voice.
2. In section A, name the 6 harmonic intervals created across the two staves.
3. In section B, name the 6 harmonic intervals in the treble staff.
4. In section B, name the 6 harmonic intervals in the bass staff.

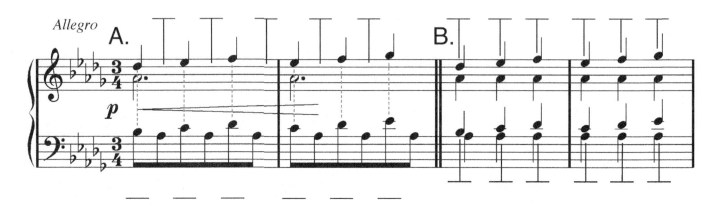

Section A: Valse Oubliée #3 by Franz Liszt. Composed in 1883.

(Section B is a simplified version of Section A. It is arranged as four voices with the alto voice repeating and the bass notes split into two voices and placed on each beat.)

5. In section A, the soprano voice moves by what interval number? _____
   The harmonic intervals here are constant at what interval number? _____
   Therefore, the bottom notes of these harmonic intervals move by _____.
6. In section B, notice exactly how the harmonic intervals widen in each staff.
   The lower voice remains on the same pitch while the upper voice moves.
   Oblique motion: One voice remaining stationary while the other moves.
7. In section B, notice the tenor voice moving in the same direction as the soprano.
   Though they remain a 10th apart (steps 2 & 5), the interval qualities change.
   Similar motion: Two voices moving in the same direction but by different interval distances.
8. A. Play sections A and B in the treble staff.
   B. Play sections A and B in the bass staff.
   C. Play both sections, hands together, thinking of the discoveries in steps 5 - 8.
   D. What thoughts or feelings does section A evoke?

Music Analysis Activity #10

1. On the top lines, name the melodic interval between each soprano note.
2. On the next lines, name the melodic interval between each alto note.
3. Below the bass staff, name each harmonic interval.

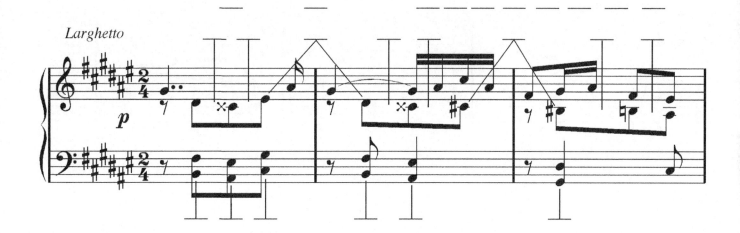

Sonatine by Maurice Ravel. Composed in 1905.

4. The most prevalent interval in the soprano voice is the _____.
5. The most prevalent interval in the alto voice is the _____.
6. In the bass staff, all of the harmonic intervals are perfect 5ths. The notes in each harmonic interval are moving in the same direction by the same amount. Examine these intervals, melodically, to see how this is true.
   Parallel motion: a. Two voices moving in the same direction by the same interval. b. The interval between two voices staying exactly the same.
7. What is the interval between the first alto note and the "tenor" note directly below it? _____ Is this interval constant whenever the alto voice and tenor voices are played simultaneously? What type of motion exists between the alto and tenor voice? _____
8. A. Play the treble staff, thinking of the discoveries in steps 4 - 5.
   B. Play the bass staff, thinking of the discovery in step 6.
   C. Play hands together, thinking of the discovery in step 7.
   D. What thoughts or feelings does this music evoke?

Music Analysis Activity #11

1. Name each melodic interval in the alto voice.
2. Name each melodic interval in the tenor voice.

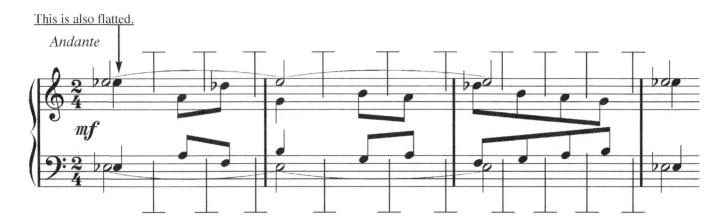

Whole Tone Scale, Mikrokosmos #136 by Bela Bartok. Composed between 1926 and 1937.

3. Only five different keys are played in the each hand. The treble-staff notes, combined, are all major 2nds apart. The bass-staff notes, combined, are also major 2nds apart.

4. This piece is called *Whole Tone Scale* because its notes are from a scale that is composed of only whole tones (major 2nds).

5. Notice how both melodies move the same distance at the same time. Each interval in one staff is a mirror inversion of that in the other staff. The interval name is not always the same (enharmonic equivalents), but the half step distance is exactly the same. The symmetry of this passage reveals an expanded definition for the word *mirror*.

6. **Mirror:** ". . . performed in inversion with respect to the intervals of each part. . . as if it were being performed from a mirror held below the notation" (Harvard Concise Dictionary of Music). A mirror could be held below either staff and you would see the interval movements of the other staff.

7. What kind of motion occurs between the alto and tenor voices? _____

8. A. Play the treble staff, thinking of the discoveries in steps 3 - 4.

   B. Play the bass staff, thinking of the discoveries in steps 3 - 4.

   C. Play hands together, thinking of the discoveries in steps 5 - 7.

   D. What thoughts or feelings does this music evoke?

Music Analysis Activity #12

1. Name the harmonic intervals within each chord. Move from bottom to top, including the interval which crosses the staves.
2. Name the indicated melodic intervals in the treble staff.

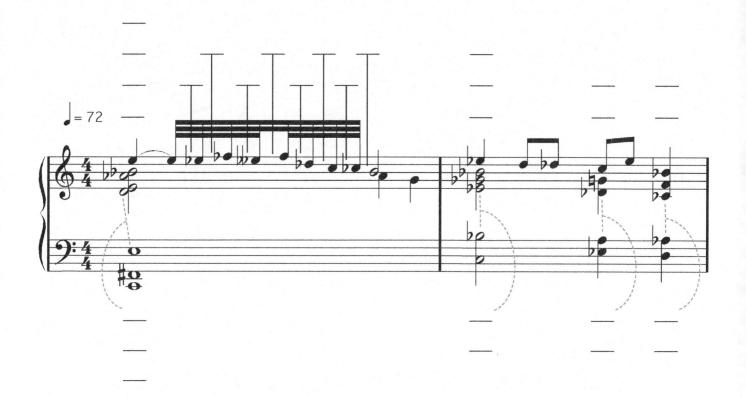

Pastorale, Trois Piéces pour Piano, by Francis Poulenc (1899 - 1963).

3. The most prevalent interval number in these chords is the _____.
4. In the first chord, the highest and lowest intervals are both _____.
5. The most prevalent 4th interval in these chords is the _____.
6. Notice that the bottom interval in each chord is dissonant. Are most of the intervals within these chords dissonant? _____
7. There is one chord whose structure suggests consonance. That chord is in measure number _____ on beat number _____.
8. A. Play the treble staff.
   B. Play the bass staff.
   C. Play hands together, thinking of the discoveries in steps 3 - 7.
   D. What thoughts or feelings does this music evoke?

Music Analysis Activity #13

1. Name each melodic interval, whether simple or compound. Name the last
   four intervals on the lower staff harmonically.

A.   B.

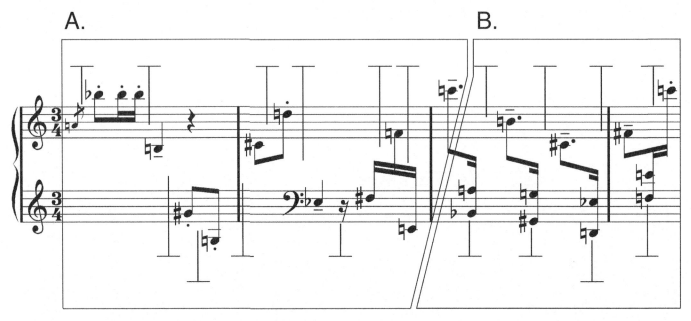

Piano Piece, Opus Posth. by Anton von Webern (1883 - 1945).

2. How many minor 9ths are there? _____ Which interval here is the enharmonic
   equivalent of the m9? _____ Which interval here is related to the m9? _____

3. How many major 7ths are there? _____ Which intervals here are enharmonic
   equivalents of the M7, or related to it, or both? _____

4. On a piece of paper, write down all the note names in group A.
   How many different names are there? _____

5. On the same piece of paper, write down all the note names in group B.
   How many different names are there? _____
   There are only twelve notes within any octave. Each group uses all twelve.

6. **Twelve-tone** or **Dodecaphonic** (from Greek *dodeka*, 'twelve')**:** Music which
   uses all 12 notes of the chromatic scale, but in some arrangement or sequence.
   The two groups have the same note order, but the notes in the second group
   are, for the most part, transposed to different octaves and played harmonically
   with a new rhythm. Can you see the repeating pattern of notes?

7. A. Play hands together, thinking of the discoveries in steps 4 - 6.
   B. What thoughts or feelings does this music evoke?

Music Analysis Activity #14

1. Name the melodic intervals in the soprano voice.
2. Name the harmonic intervals within each chord. Move from bottom to top, omitting the interval which crosses the staves.

Very Early by Bill Evans (1929 - 1980). Arranged by Barry Michael Wehrli.

3. The most prevalent harmonic interval is the _____.
4. The second most prevelant harmonic interval is the _____.
5. Notice the chords in the first and third measures. Their structure is made up of only perfect intervals and mostly perfect 4ths at that.

   Quartal Harmony: Harmonic structures (intervals/chords) based on the 4th. Use of the 4th as a building block in harmony grew in the early 20th century. Quartal harmony is a popular tool for voicing chords in jazz, as shown above. (*Tertian harmony*, based on the 3rd, is still more common. Centuries of continued use has reinforced tertain harmony as a mainstay in Western music.)

6. A. Play the treble staff, thinking of the discoveries in steps 3 - 4.
   B. Play the bass staff, thinking of the discoveries in steps 3 - 4.
   C. Play hands together, thinking of the discovery in step 5.
   D. What thoughts or feelings does this music evoke?

Music Analysis Activity #15

1. Name each melodic interval in the treble staff.
2. Name the melodic interval between each of the lowest bass-staff notes.
3. Name the harmonic intervals within each chord, moving from bottom to top.

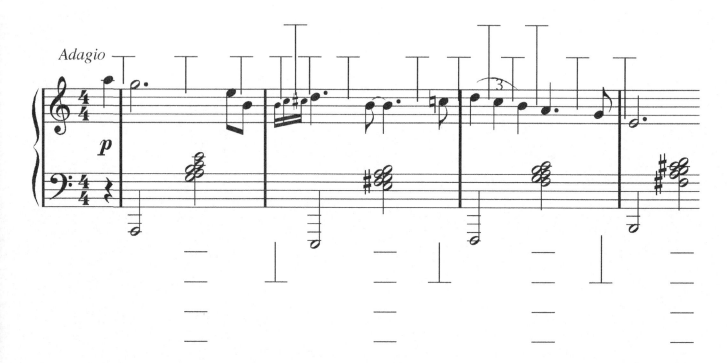

Crystal Silence by Chick Corea (1941 -). Arranged by Barry Michael Wehrli.

4. The most prevalent interval number in the treble staff is the _____.
   Being melodic intervals, they do not sound dissonant for the most part.
5. The most prevalent interval number in the chords is the _____.
   These chords are composed of dissonant-sounding harmonic intervals.
6. **Cluster** or **Tone cluster:** A dissonant group of major or minor 2nds played
   together as a chord. (These chords can include other intervals as well.)
   The above chords are "five-note clusters," as they contain five notes.
7. The only interval number in these clusters other than the 2nd is the _____.
8. A. Play the treble staff, thinking of the discovery in step 4.
   B. Play the bass staff, thinking of the discoveries in steps 5 - 7.
   C. Play hands together.
   D. What thoughts or feelings does this music evoke?

Mastering Intervals

Edition 3

Answer Manual

Barry Michael Wehrli

Melodic & Harmonic Interval Activity #1
(Page 3)

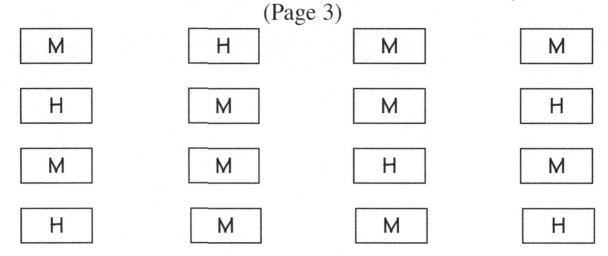

Stemming Intervals Activity #1
(Page 6)

Stemming Intervals Activity #2
(Page 7)

Interval Number Activity #2
(Page 9)

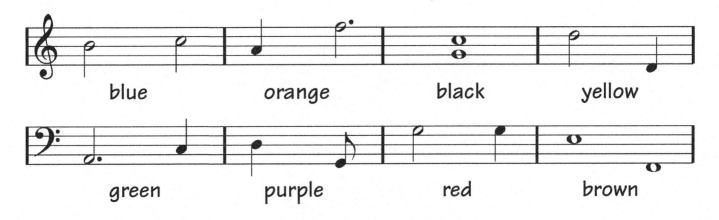

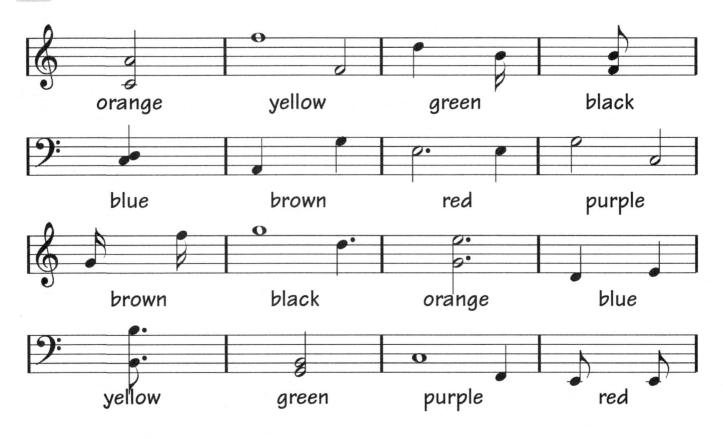

Interval Number Activity #3
(Page 10)

3rd	2nd	6th	4th
unison	5th	octave	7th
4th	3rd	6th	unison
5th	2nd	octave	7th
4th	7th	3rd	2nd
5th	octave	unison	6th

Interval Number Activity #4
(Page 11)

Check written work.

Interval Number Activity #5
(Page 12)

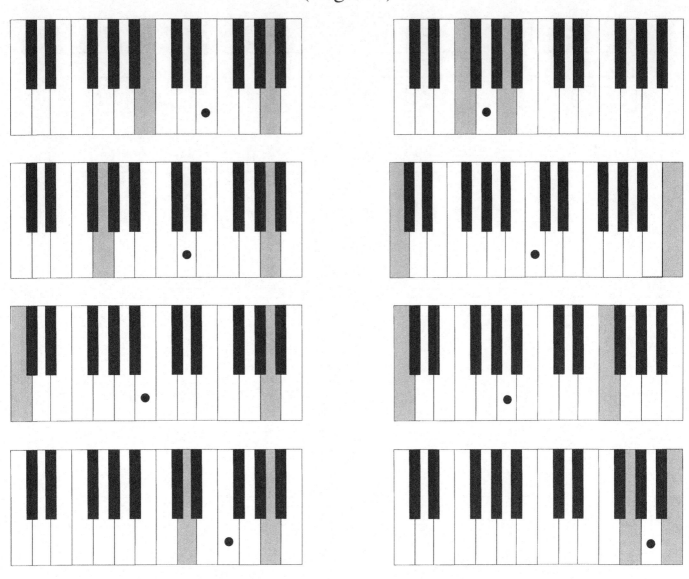

Interval Number Activity #6
(Page 13)

1. __A__ .   7. __D__ .   13. __G__ .   19. __C__ .   25. __E__ .
2. __E__ .   8. __F__ .   14. __D__ .   20. __F__ .   26. __D__ .
3. __G__ .   9. __B__ .   15. __B__ .   21. __F__ .   27. __D__ .
4. __B__ .   10. __F__ .   16. __C__ .   22. __E__ .   28. __A__ .
5. __C__ .   11. __E__ .   17. __B__ .   23. __A__ .   29. __C__ .
6. __A__ .   12. __C__ .   18. __G__ .   24. __G__ .   30. __D__ .

Perfect Interval Activity #2
(Page 16)

P4	P1	P8	P5
P1	P8	P4	P5
P8	P5	P4	P1

Perfect Interval Activity #3
(Page 17)

Perfect Interval Activity #4
(Page 18)

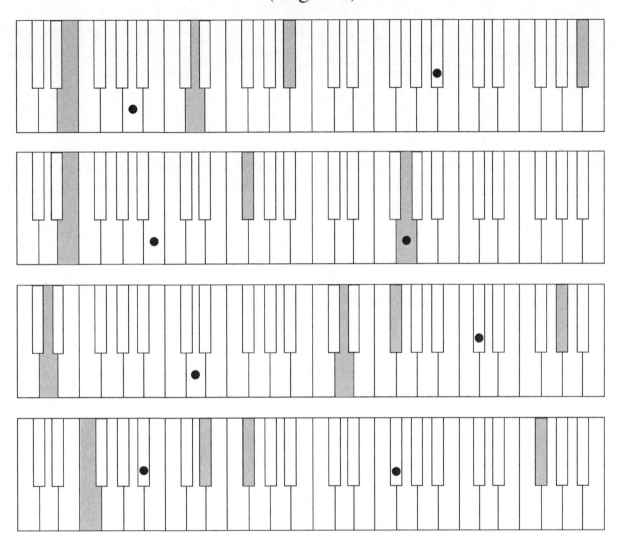

Perfect Interval Activity #5
(Page 20)

1. ___F×___.
2. ___F___.
3. ___D___.
4. ___B___.
5. ___A♭___.
6. ___G___.
7. ___A#___.

8. ___C___.
9. ___B♭___.
10. ___E♭___.
11. ___A#___.
12. ___C#___.
13. ___C♭♭___.
14. ___D♭___.

15. ___D___.
16. ___G#___.
17. ___E___.
18. ___G___.
19. ___C#___.
20. ___C×___.

Major Interval Activity #2
(Pages 24-25)

Major Interval Activity #3
(Page 26)

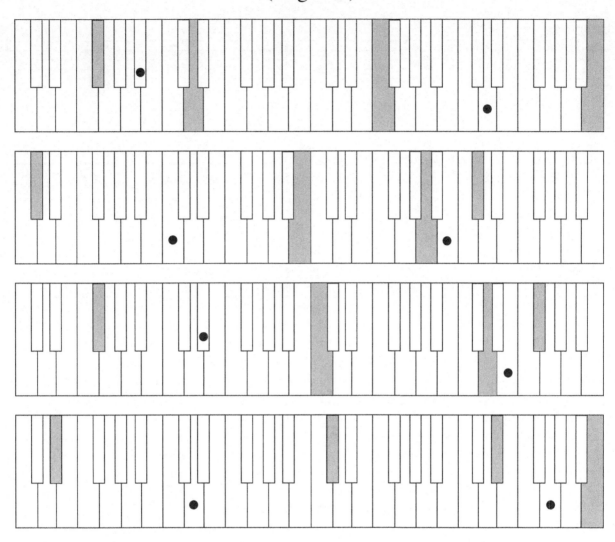

Major Interval Activity #4
(Page 29)

1. _____D#_____.
2. _____Gb_____.
3. _____B_____.
4. _____D_____.
5. _____Cb_____.
6. _____F#_____.
7. _____C#_____.

8. _____A_____.
9. _____C#_____.
10. _____Ebb_____.
11. _____F#_____.
12. _____E_____.
13. _____Db_____.
14. _____C_____.

15. _____E#_____.
16. _____F_____.
17. _____G#_____.
18. _____Cbb_____.
19. _____A#_____.
20. _____Gb_____.

116

Minor Interval Activity #2
(Pages 32-33)

Minor Interval Activity #3
(Page 34)

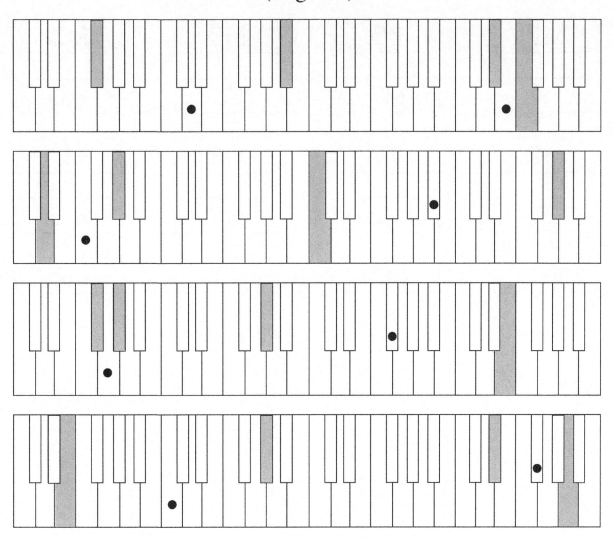

Minor Interval Activity #4
(Page 37)

1. ___ B♭ ___.
2. ___ B ___.
3. ___ F♭ ___.
4. ___ E ___.
5. ___ D# ___.
6. ___ C ___.
7. ___ A♭ ___.

8. ___ D♭ ___.
9. ___ G♭ ___.
10. ___ A♭ ___.
11. ___ E ___.
12. ___ B♭♭ ___.
13. ___ A ___.
14. ___ G# ___.

15. ___ C# ___.
16. ___ A# ___.
17. ___ A ___.
18. ___ E♭ ___.
19. ___ F ___.
20. ___ D ___.

Mixed Interval Activity #2
(Page 40)

M2	P8	m3	M3
P4	M7	P5	m6
m2	P1	M6	M7
P5	M2	m7	m3
P8	M3	m7	m6

Mixed Interval Activity #3
(Page 41)

Mixed Interval Activity #4
(Page 42)

Mixed Interval Activity #5
(Page 43)

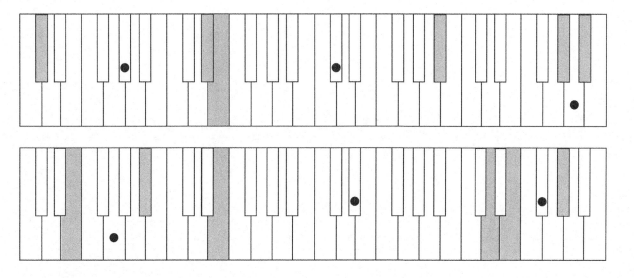

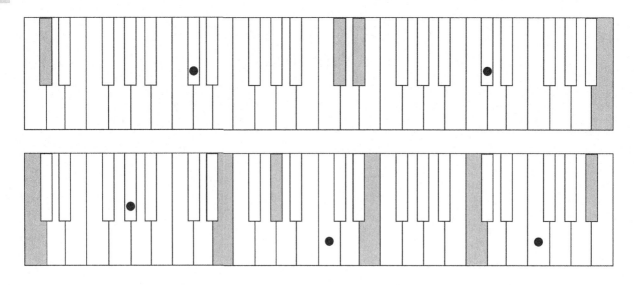

Augmented Interval Activity #2
(Pages 45-47)

122

Augmented Interval Activity #3
(Page 48)

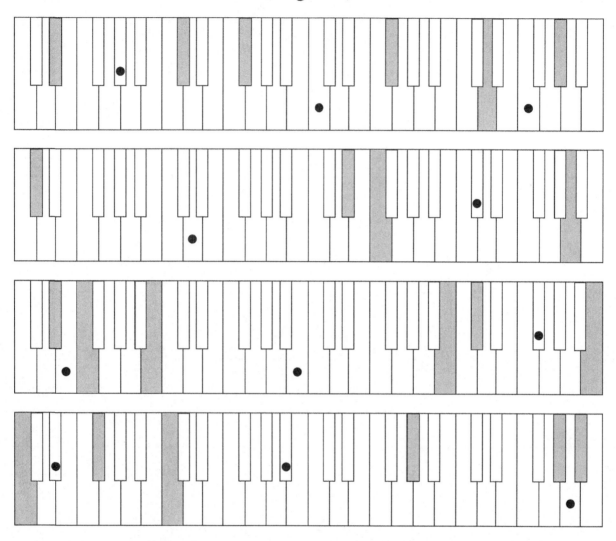

Augmented Interval Activity #4
(Page 50)

1. A#
2. E♭
3. A✕
4. G♭
5. A
6. F
7. C#

8. B♭
9. E♭♭
10. F✕
11. F♭
12. A♭
13. A♭♭
14. F#

15. B
16. G#
17. D♮
18. C
19. A#
20. G

Diminished Interval Activity #2
(Pages 53-55)

124

Diminished Interval Activity #3
(Pages 56)

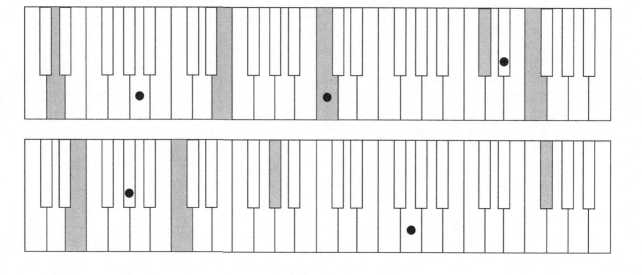

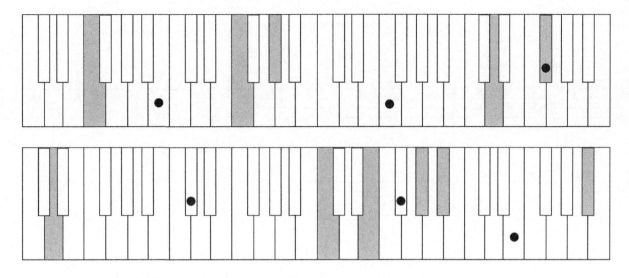

Diminished Interval Activity #4
(Page 57)

1. A^b
2. $D^\#$
3. D^b
4. $D^\#$
5. A^b
6. $F^\times$
7. B^{bb}

8. C
9. D^b
10. $F^\#$
11. C^b
12. $A^\times$
13. G
14. B

15. $C^\times$
16. $E^\#$
17. $A^\#$
18. E^{bb}
19. G^b
20. E

Mixed Interval Activity #7
(Page 58)

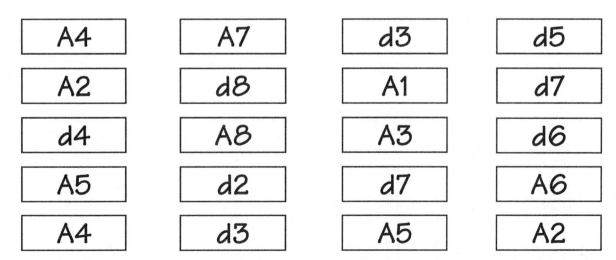

A4	A7	d3	d5
A2	d8	A1	d7
d4	A8	A3	d6
A5	d2	d7	A6
A4	d3	A5	A2

126

Mixed Interval Activity #8
(Page 59)

Mixed Interval Activity #9
(Page 60)

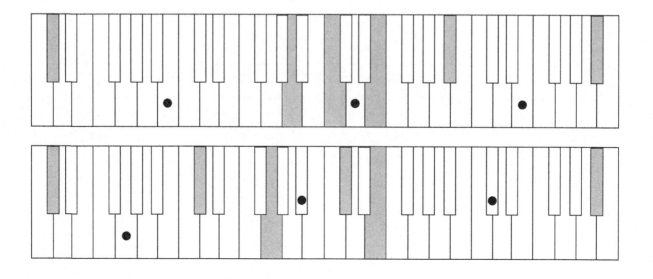

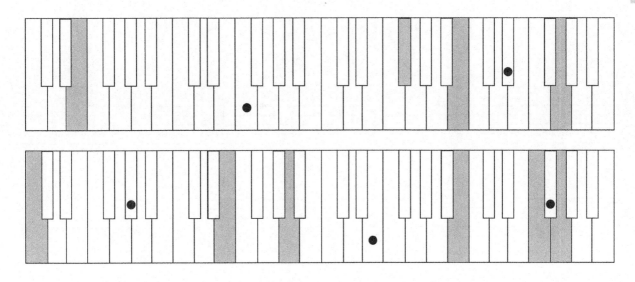

Mixed Interval Activity #10
(Page 63)

Mixed Interval Activity #11
(Page 64)

Mixed Interval Activity #12
(Pages 65-66)

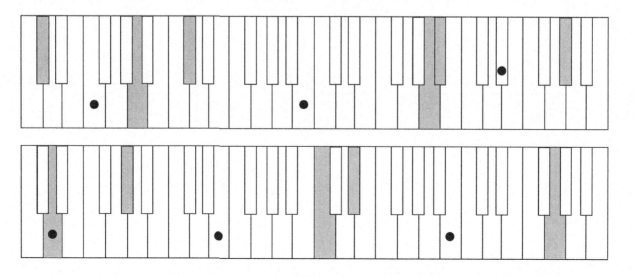

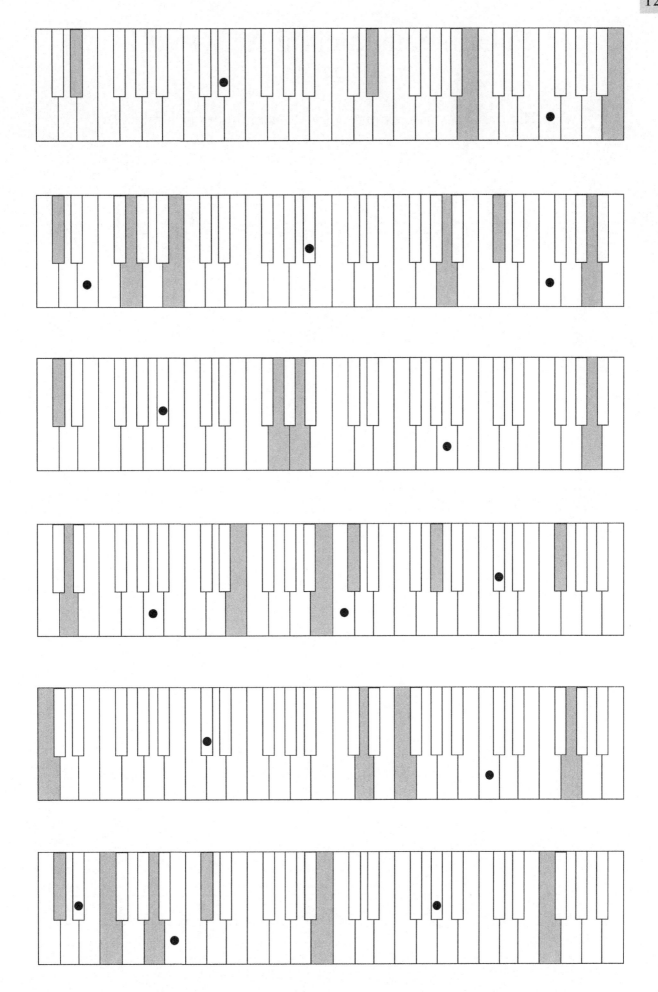

Enharmonic Interval Activity #1
(Page 71)

The order of answers may vary for each interval number.

Mixed Interval Final Exam

The order of answers may vary for each interval number.

(Page 72)

P1 = C to C
P1 = D♭♭ to D♭♭
P1 = B♯ to B♯
d2 = C to D♭♭
d2 = B♯ to C

A1 = A♯ to A✕
A1 = B♭ to B♮
A1 = C♭♭ to C♭
m2 = B♭ to C♭
m2 = A♯ to B

M2 = D to E
M2 = C✕ to D✕
M2 = E♭♭ to F♭
d3 = D to F♭
d3 = C✕ to E

A2 = G♯ to A✕
A2 = A♭ to B
m3 = G♯ to B
m3 = A♭ to C♭

(Page 73)

M3 = G to B
M3 = F✕ to A✕
M3 = A♭♭ to C♭
d4 = F✕ to B
d4 = G to C♭

A3 = A to C✕
A3 = B♭♭ to D
P4 = A to D
P4 = G✕ to C✕
P4 = B♭♭ to E♭♭

A4 = E to A♯
A4 = F♭ to B♭
d5 = E to B♭
d5 = D✕ to A♯
d5 = F♭ to C♭♭

P5 = E♭ to B♭
P5 = D♯ to A♯
P5 = F♭♭ to C♭♭
d6 = D♯ to B♭
d6 = E♭ to C♭♭

A5 = A to E♯
A5 = B♭♭ to F
m6 = A to F
m6 = G✕ to E♯
m6 = B♭♭ to G♭♭

(Page 74)

M6 = E♭ to C
M6 = D♯ to B♯
M6 = F♭♭ to D♭♭
d7 = E♭ to D♭♭
d7 = D♯ to C

A6 = G to E♯
A6 = A♭♭ to F
m7 = G to F
m7 = F✕ to E♯
m7 = A♭♭ to G♭♭

M7 = D to C♯
M7 = C✕ to B✕
M7 = E♭♭ to D♭
d8 = D to D♭
d8 = C✕ to C♯

A7 = G♭ to F♯
A7 = F♯ to E✕
P8 = F♯ to F♯
P8 = G♭ to G♭
P8 = E✕ to E✕

A8 = E to E♯
A8 = F♭ to F

Harmonic Inversion Activity #2
(Page 77)

1. m3 = __M6__
2. A7 = __d2__
3. P5 = __P4__
4. d8 = __A1__
5. A6 = __d3__
6. d6 = __A3__
7. P4 = __P5__
8. M2 = __m7__
9. d2 = __A7__

10. P1 = __P8__
11. A2 = __d7__
12. d5 = __A4__
13. m2 = __M7__
14. A3 = __d6__
15. M6 = __m3__
16. d4 = __A5__
17. A1 = __d8__
18. m7 = __M2__

19. P8 = __P1__
20. m6 = __M3__
21. M3 = __m6__
22. d7 = __A2__
23. A5 = __d4__
24. M7 = __m2__
25. A4 = __d5__
26. d3 = __A6__

Harmonic Inversion Activity #3
(Page 78)

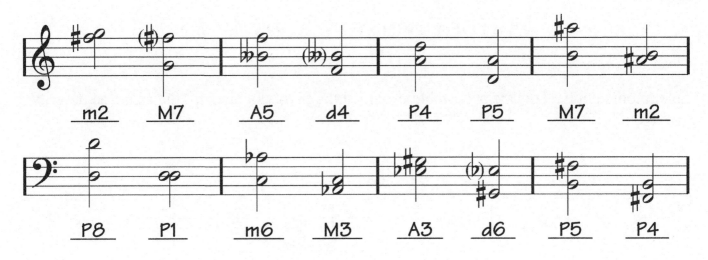

P8 P1 m6 M3 A3 d6 P5 P4

Harmonic Inversion Activity #4
(Page 79)

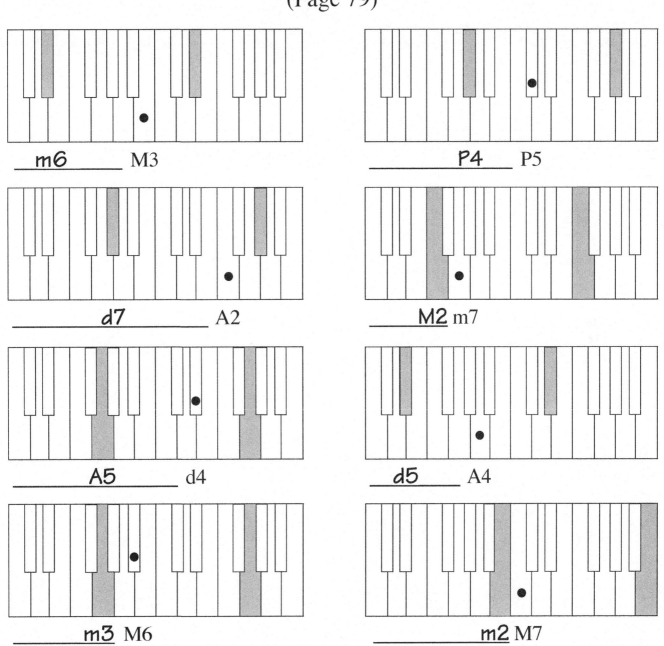

m6 M3

P4 P5

d7 A2

M2 m7

A5 d4

d5 A4

m3 M6

m2 M7

Mirror Inversion Activity #1
(Page 81)

Enharmonic equivalents are acceptable provided the pivot note is kept the same, as described on page 80.

Compound Interval Activity #1
(Page 83)

1. d9 = __d2__
2. P12 = __P5__
3. M13 = __M6__
4. A11 = __A4__
5. m14 = __m7__
6. M10 = __M3__
7. P15 = __P8__
8. m13 = __m6__

9. A12 = __A5__
10. d14 = __d7__
11. A10 = __A3__
12. d11 = __d4__
13. A15 = __A8__
14. M9 = __M2__
15. A14 = __A7__
16. d15 = __d8__

17. M14 = __M7__
18. A13 = __A6__
19. m10 = __m3__
20. P11 = __P4__
21. d12 = __d5__
22. A9 = __A2__
23. m9 = __m2__
24. d10 = __d3__

1. m3 = __m10__
2. A7 = __A14__
3. P5 = __P12__
4. M2 = __M9__
5. A6 = __A13__
6. d6 = __d13__
7. P4 = __P11__
8. A8 = __A15__

9. d2 = __d9__
10. m7 = __m14__
11. d5 = __d12__
12. m2 = __m9__
13. A3 = __A10__
14. M6 = __M13__
15. d4 = __d11__
16. A2 = __A9__

17. P8 = __P15__
18. m6 = __m13__
19. M3 = __M10__
20. d7 = __d14__
21. A5 = __A12__
22. M7 = __M14__
23. A4 = __A11__
24. d3 = __d10__

Compound Interval Activity #2
(Page 84)

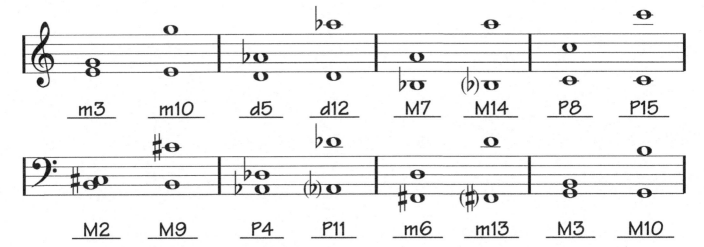

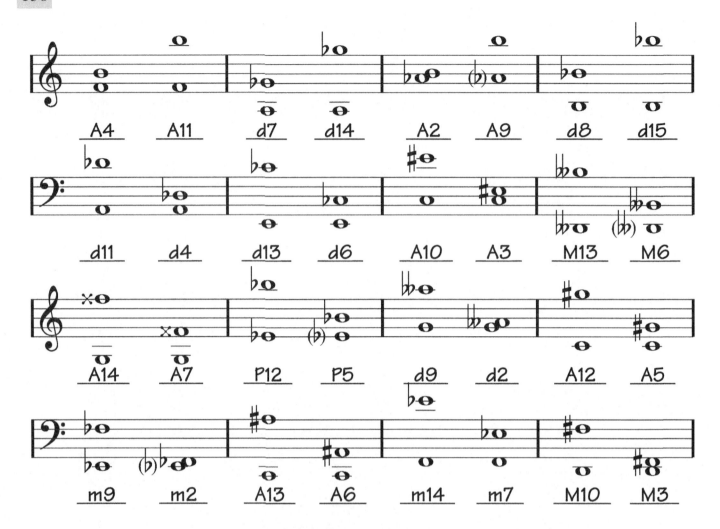

Compound Interval Activity #3
(Page 85)

1. ___B___.
2. ___D#___.
3. ___C___.
4. ___A#___.
5. ___C#___.
6. ___Db___.
7. ___D___.

8. ___Bbb___.
9. ___G___.
10. ___Cb___.
11. ___Db___.
12. ___E___.
13. ___B___.
14. ___Gbb___.

15. ___E×___.
16. ___G#___.
17. ___F×___.
18. ___C#___.
19. ___F#___.
20. ___A___.

Music Analysis Activity #1
(Page 92)

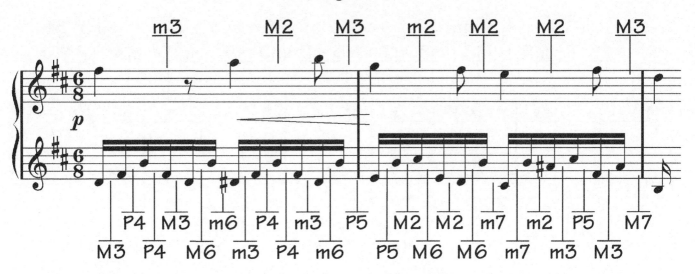

3. What are the only two interval numbers used in the upper staff melody?
   __2nd__   __3rd__

Music Analysis Activity #2
(Page 93)

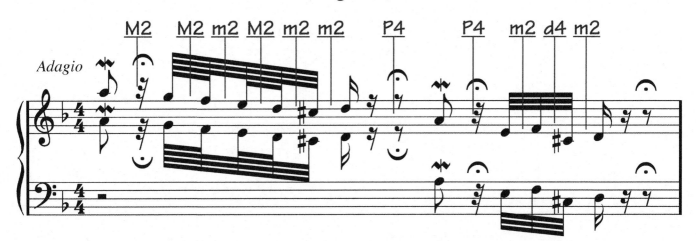

2. What are the only two interval numbers in this melody? __2nd__   __4th__
3. Notice the mordent symbols (✷) on beats 1 and 3.
   Mordent: A quick melodic movement from the principal note (shown), down
   a diatonic step and back up. This movement produced what interval? __M2__
4. What is the interval from the first eighth note to the first sixteenth? __P5__
   What is the interval from the second eighth to the second sixteenth? __P5__

Music Analysis Activity #3
(Page 94)

3. The most prevalent (frequently occurring) interval in the treble staff is the __m3__ .
4. The most prevelant compound interval in the bass staff is the __m10__ .

Music Analysis Activity #4
(Page 95)

4. The most prevalent interval in the melody is the ___m2___ .

Music Analysis Activity #5
(Page 96)

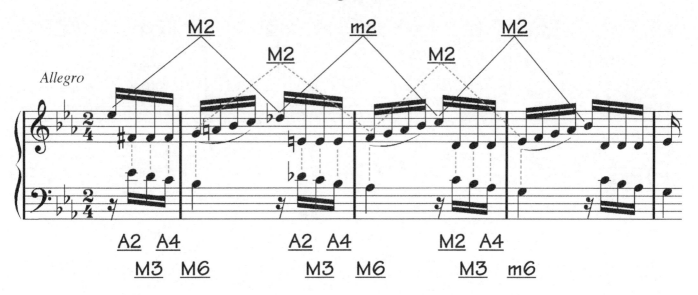

3. On beat 1 of each full measure, the melody in the treble staff drops by what interval? __M2__ On beat 2 of each measure, the melody in the treble staff drops by what two types of intervals? __M2__ __m2__

Music Analysis Activity #6
(Page 97)

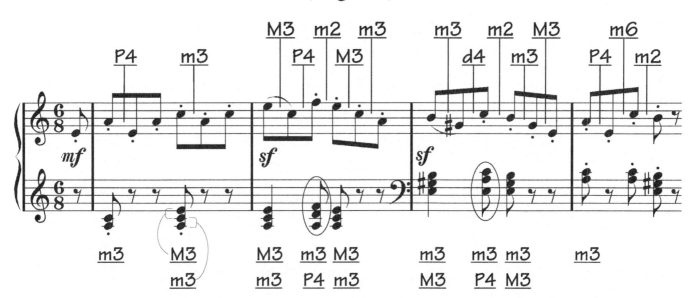

3. Notice the sequence in the upper staff, third measure. This repeated phrase from the second measure drops by what interval? __P4__
4. The accompaniment also drops at the same time by what amount? __P4__ The third measure demonstrates what type of sequence? __harmonic__

Music Analysis Activity #7
(Page 98)

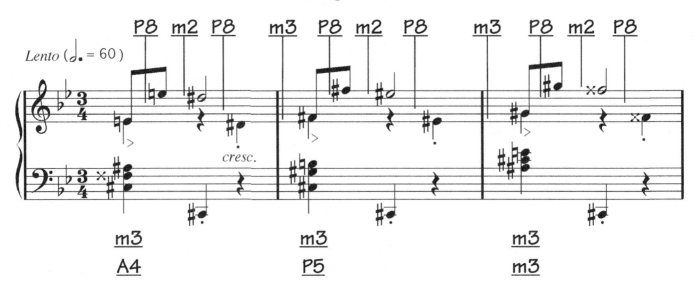

3. Notice the sequence in the treble-staff melody. From measure to measure, this melodic sequence is shifting up by what interval? __M2__

5. The most prevalent interval in the bass-staff chords is the __m3__.
   These chords have structures similar to those in the Schumann excerpt. Looking at the first chord, if we invert the top two notes down (or the bottom one up) the resulting chord is made up of stacked __3rds__.

Music Analysis Activity #8
(Page 99)

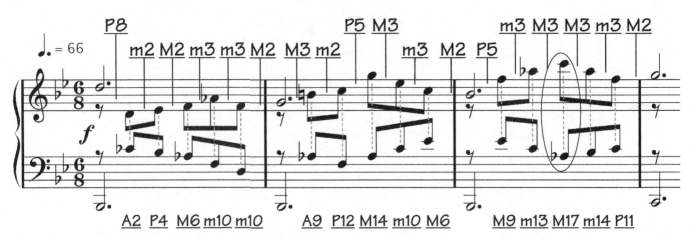

3. The most prevalent interval number in the treble staff is the __3rd__.

5. Looking at the melodic intervals in the bass staff, what is the most prevalent interval number? __3rd__

Music Analysis Activity #9
(Page 100)

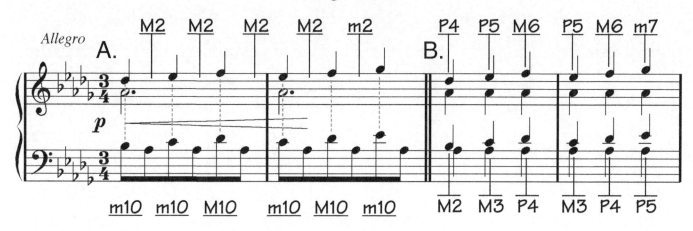

5. In section A, the soprano voice moves by what interval number? __2nd__
   The harmonic intervals here are constant at what interval number? __10th__
   Therefore, the bottom notes of these harmonic intervals move by __2nds__.

Music Analysis Activity #10
(Page 101)

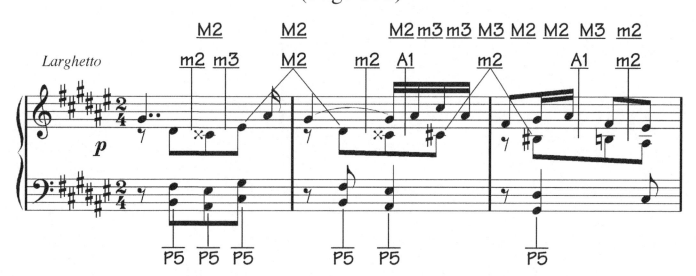

4. The most prevalent interval in the soprano voice is the __M2__.
5. The most prevalent interval in the alto voice is the __m2__.
7. What is the interval between the first alto note and the "tenor" note directly below it? __M6__ Is this interval constant whenever the alto voice and tenor voices are played simultaneously? What type of motion exists between the alto and tenor voice? __parallel__

Music Analysis Activity #11
(Page 102)

7. What kind of motion occurs between the alto and tenor voices? __contrary__

Music Analysis Activity #12
(Page 103)

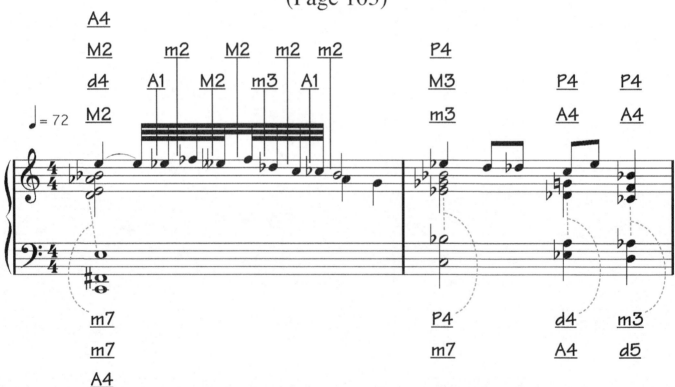

3. The most prevalent interval number in these chords is the __4th__.

4. In the first chord, the highest and lowest intervals are both __A4__.

5. The most prevalent 4th interval in these chords is the __A4__.

6. Notice that the bottom interval in each chord is dissonant. Are most of the intervals within these chords dissonant? __yes__

7. There is one chord whose structure suggests consonance. That chord is in measure number __2__ on beat number __1__.

Music Analysis Activity #13
(Page 104)

A.   **B.**

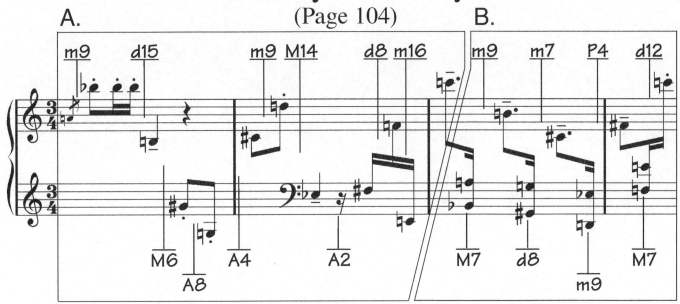

2. How many minor 9ths are there? __4__ Which interval here is the enharmonic
   equivalent of the m9? __A8__ Which interval here is related to the m9? __m16__
3. How many major 7ths are there? __2__ Which intervals here are enharmonic
   equivalents of the M7, or related to it, or both? __d8, M14, d15__ (respective order)
4. On a piece of paper, write down all the note names in group A.
   How many different names are there? __12__
5. On the same piece of paper, write down all the note names in group B.
   How many different names are there? __12__

Music Analysis Activity #14
(Page 105)

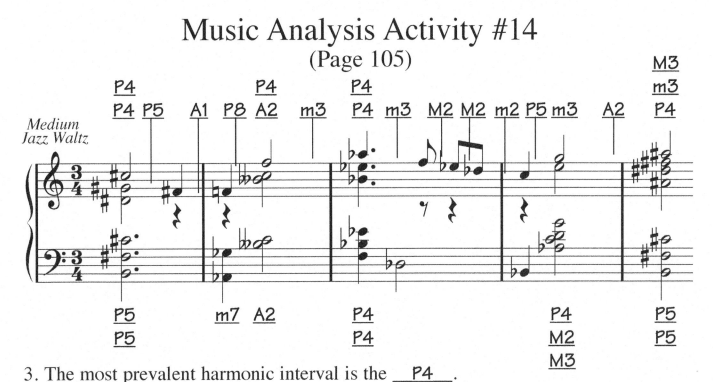

3. The most prevalent harmonic interval is the __P4__.
4. The second most prevalent harmonic interval is the __P5__.

Music Analysis Activity #15
(Page 106)

4. The most prevalent interval number in the treble staff is the __2nd__.
5. The most prevalent interval number in the chords is the __2nd__.
7. The only interval number in these clusters other than the 2nd is the __3rd__.

Interval Ear Training Resources

(alphabetically by product name)

PRODUCT NAME	CREATOR	FORMAT	WEB ADDRESS	PRICE
Aural Skills Trainer	Vincent Oddo	Mac/PC	www.ecsmedia.com	$39.95
Big Ears	Michael Ossmann	Online	www.ossmann.com/bigears	Free
Ear Master Pro	MidiTec	Mac/PC	www.earmaster.com	$59.99
Ear Trainer	Martin Schoeberl	Online	www.good-ear.com	Free
Ear Training Coach	Adventus	PC	www.adventus.com	$34.95 (each)
Ear Training Expedition-Part 1	Trail Creek Systems	PC	www.trailcreeksystems.com	$79.95
Ear Training for Instrumentalists	Homespun	6 Audio CDs	www.homespuntapes.com	$59.95
Earope	Cope Media	PC	www.cope.dk	$47.00
Eartraining	L. Peters	Mac	www.lpeters.de	Free
Essentials of Music Theory-Vol.2	Alfred Publishing	Mac/PC	www.alfred.com	$105.00
Interval Ear Trainer	Musictheory.net	Online or Mac Freeware	www.musictheory.net	Free
Listen	Imaja	Mac (OS 9)	www.imaja.com/listen	$79.95
Music Lessons 1	Mibac Music Software	Mac/PC	www.mibac.com	Mac $123.00 PC $93.00
Music Theory Builder	G. David Peters	Mac/PC	www.ecsmedia.com	$59.95
Pitch ID	KBA Software	PC	www.musicstudy.com	$18.95
Practica Musica	Ars Nova Software	Mac/PC	www.ars-nova.com	$100.00
Relative Pitch Ear Training SuperCourse	David Lucas Burge	41 Audio CDs	www.RelativePitch.com	$299.00

NOTE:

Many of the above products have not been tested for conformity to the ear training activities in this book. Research any product carefully before buying. Prices subject to change. An online search under "ear training" or "intervals" may provide other options.

Mastering Intervals
Edition 3
Glossary

Articulation: The manner in which keys are played and then released which gives a performance expression, clarity and definition.

Chord: A group of three or more tones played together; also thought of as of two or more intervals played together. The most common interval between chord tones is the third.

Chromatically; Chromatic: A series of notes moving by half steps.

Composition: a. An individual piece of music, b. The process of creating a piece of music.

Diatonic: Of or belonging to the given key or scale; notes that are part of the scale. (See *scale*.) C, D, E, F, G, A, B are all diatonic notes in the C Major scale.

Double Flat (♭♭): A symbol lowering the pitch of a natural note by one whole step or lowering a flatted note by one additional half step. On the keyboard, A♭♭ and G are the same key.

Double Sharp (✕): A symbol raising the pitch of a natural note by one whole step or raising a sharped note by one additional half step. On the keyboard, A✕ and B are the same key.

Dynamics: The aspect of music relating to volume; loudness or softness.

Expression: The qualities in music which produce emotion and feeling such as degrees of loudness, changes in speed, touch of the keys, use of the pedals, and so on.

Half Step: The smallest interval in Western music; on a keyboard, the distance from one key to the *very next,* whether white or black. Two half steps equal one **whole step**.

Harmony: a. Two or more musical tones played simultaneously; the vertical aspect of musical texture, as opposed to the horizontal aspect which is melody, b. The structure and function of chords.

Improvisation: The art of creating music spontaneously during performance, without rehearsal or preparation. It is often based on a subject, theme, or idea.

Key: The center or main note in a musical composition that determines which scale is used. The tonic of a scale is also called the "keynote". When a composition is in the "key of A Major", it means the composition is based on the A Major scale.

Major scale: A scale having the following pattern of whole steps and half steps:

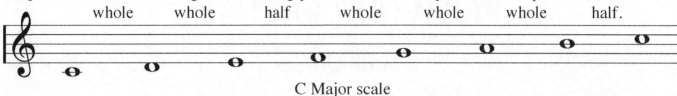

whole   whole   half   whole   whole   whole   half.

C Major scale

Minor scale, Harmonic: A scale having the following pattern of whole steps and half steps:

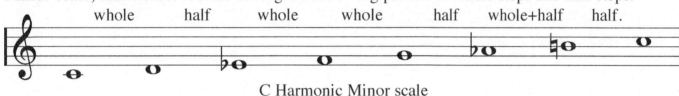

whole   half   whole   whole   half   whole+half   half.

C Harmonic Minor scale

Minor scale, Melodic: A scale having the following pattern of whole steps and half steps:

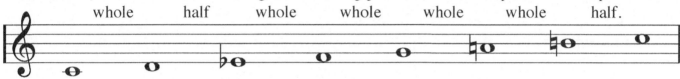

whole   half   whole   whole   whole   whole   half.

C Melodic Minor scale (ascending form)

NOTE: The descending form lowers the 6th and 7th scale degrees, equivalent to the natural minor.

Minor scale, Natural: A scale having the following pattern of whole steps and half steps:

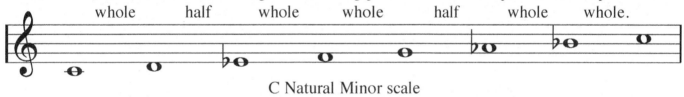

whole   half   whole   whole   half   whole   whole.

C Natural Minor scale

Octave: A general term meaning the perfect octave; the distance of 12 half steps.

Root: The note a chord is built upon.

Scale: Whole steps and half steps arranged in a pattern within an octave. A scale is named by its tonic plus the name given to its pattern of whole and half steps.

Scale Degrees: The number and name given to each scale tone, relating its distance to the tonic.

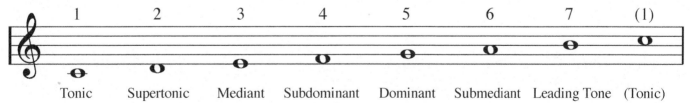

1   2   3   4   5   6   7   (1)

Tonic   Supertonic   Mediant   Subdominant   Dominant   Submediant   Leading Tone   (Tonic)

Tempo: The speed of music; the speed of musical beats.

Tonic: The note a scale is built upon.

Mastering Intervals
Edition 3

Bibliography

Grout, Donald Jay. A History of Western Music. 3rd ed. New York: W. W. Norton & Company, Inc., 1980.

Harder, Paul O. Harmonic Materials in Tonal Music, Part 1. 5th ed. Newton: Allyn and Bacon, Inc., 1985.

Heussenstamm, George. The Norton Manual of Music Notation. New York: W. W. Norton & Company, Inc., 1987.

Hindley, Geoffrey, ed. The Larousse Encyclopedia of Music. New Jersey: Chartwell Books, Inc., 1977.

Humphries, Carl. The Piano Handbook. San Francisco: Backbeat Books, 2002.

Kennan, Kent. Counterpoint. 3rd ed. New Jersey: Prentice-Hall, Inc., 1987.

Lloyd-Watts, Valery and Carole L. Bigler. Ornamentation: A Question & Answer Manual. Van Nuys: Alfred Publishing Company, Inc., 1995.

McLean, Edwin. The FJH Classic Music Dictionary. Miami: The FJH Music Company, Inc., 1995.

Novello, John. The Contemporary Keyboardist. Miami: CPP Belwin, 1987.

Randel, Don Michael. Harvard Concise Dictionary of Music. Cambridge: Harvard UP, Belknap Press, 1978.

Read, Gardner. Music Notation: A Manual of Modern Practice. 2nd ed. New York: Taplinger Publishing Company, Inc., 1979.

Schaum, John W. Harmony Lessons, Book 1. Melville: Belwin Mills Publishing Corp., 1949.

Congratulations

You have completed

Mastering Intervals

_____

Name

_____

Date

More Cutting-Edge Books and Products
for the Music Teacher and Retailer

Piano Practice and Performance

- Designed for students and aspiring professionals.
- Four chapters present helpful and concise tips and strategies for successful practice, memorization and performance at the piano.
- Researched and tested by the authors in their own teaching practices.
- Glossary of musical terms included.
- Paperback, 68 pages.

"There is quite a degree of flexibility that acknowledges individual differences. You could quibble about the details, but the thoroughness and practicality of advice is undeniable. A very refreshing book, filling a space not occupied before in its concise format and genre."
Dr. Luiz de Moura Castro - Professor of Piano at The Hartt School, University of Hartford; international soloist and pedagogue.

Essential Piano and Keyboard Technique

- Takes early-intermediate students well into advanced levels.
- Four sections present technical exercises by type or category for easy reference.
- Contains a variety of important technical exercises in addition to the traditional scales, chords, arpeggios and cadences.
- Numerous tips on using dynamics and articulation in technical exercises.
- Exceeds the technical requirements of many state and national programs.
- Paperback, 158 pages.

"If you want a comprehensive compendium of exercises that help build almost every aspect of technique, Essential Piano and Keyboard Technique is it. This book is a treasure trove. . . logically arranged into 4 broad sections for ease of locating specific exercises. Great resource!"
Patsy Rabinowitz - NCTM; Owner, West Chester Academy of Music.

Classic Series: Volume 1 Beginning Basics for the Piano

- A holistic approach for the beginning piano student, ages seven and up.
- Five workshops guide the student from learning the names of the white keys on the keyboard through playing beginner-level arrangements of famous works by Bach, Beethoven, Mozart as well as American classics.
- Posture, ear training and sight-reading projects develop skills needed to play easily and beautifully.
- Paperback, 206 pages including 12 flashcard pages.

". . . you have done an excellent job of presenting your ideas. Teachers could use your materials to enhance their teaching. It is clear that you have thought out things carefully and presented them in a systematic way that is helpful to both teachers and students."
Dr. Jeanine Jacobson - clinician and author of *Professional Piano Teaching*.

(over)

Classic Series: Volume 2 Intermediate Basics for the Piano

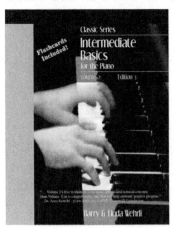

- A holistic approach that follows *Volume 1*, for the early-intermediate student.
- Five workshops introduce the student to subjects such as key signatures and accidentals, pedaling, ledger line notation, more complex rhythms and harmony.
- Music by classical and modern composers is arranged to demonstrate each subject, increasing in texture and complexity as the student progresses.
- Technical workouts develop strength and coordination.
- Paperback, 226 pages including 22 flashcard pages.

"... *Volume 2's five workshops cover more complicated musical concepts [than Volume 1] in a comprehensive way that will help students' positive progress. I would strongly recommend this Series to young teachers and self-study adults.*"
Dr. Anna Krendel - piano instructor, CAPMT District IX Coordinator.

Music Instruction Forms: 1-Year Journal

- For all instrumentalists at any level of instruction.
- A Weekly Practice Calendar establishes the student's practice days and times and the total hours to practice within the week.
- 52 Weekly Lesson Plans carry the student through a full year's study. These easy to use plans organize assignments by category and provide spaces for the sequence, duration and grading of each assignment.
- Four Quarterly Student Progress Reports assess the student's strengths and weaknesses, quarterly. Divided into eight study categories and a general comments section, these reports keep the student on track through the year.
- Completed Journals provide a running record of the student's progress.
- Paperback, 68 pages.

Ear Training: Middle C to C

- A companion compact disc to *The Classic Series Volumes 1 and 2* or for any musician looking to improve pitch recognition.
- Develops instant pitch recognition from piano middle C to the next C above.
- Each of the 14 ear training sessions adds one new pitch at a time, providing an easy learning curve.
- A pitch is given with ample time to guess the correct key name and the answer announced afterward.
- Listen in your car, at work or at home. No teacher or assistance needed.
- Over an hour of training time on one CD.

Visit us at www.wehrlipubs.com.

Wehrli Publications

Cutting-Edge Books and Products
for the Music Teacher and Retailer

12830 Burbank Boulevard, Box 204, Valley Village, CA 91607-1402 www.wehrlipubs.com